…h of SOUTHWARK with the new Additional Buildings

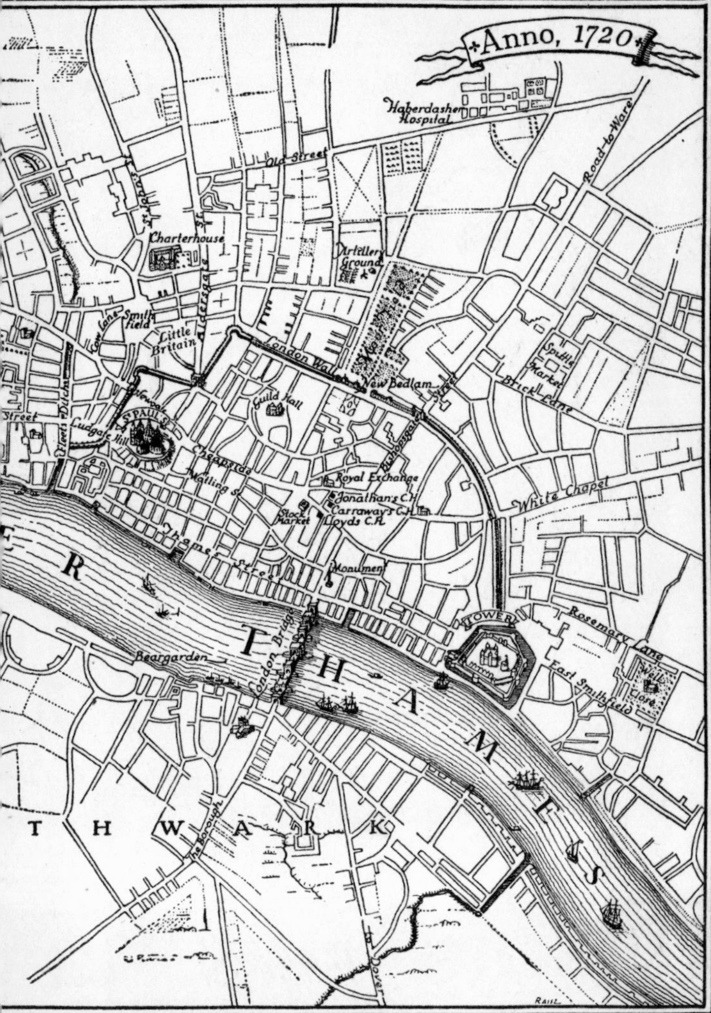

Anno, 1720

Haberdasher Hospital
Road to Ware
Old Street
St. John's St.
Charterhouse
Artillery Ground
Aldersgate St.
Cow Lane
Smithfield
Little Britain
London Wall
Moorfields
New Bedlam
Street
Spittle Market
Brick Lane
Guild Hall
Newgate
St. PAUL'S
Street
Fleet Ditch
Ludgate Hill
Cheapside
Watling St.
Bishopsgate
Royal Exchange
Jonathan's C.H.
Carraway's C.H.
Stock Market
Lloyds C.H.
White Chapel
Thames Street
Monument
TOWER
Rosemary Lane
Well Close
East Smithfield
Beargarden
London Bridge
R T H A M E S
T H W A R K
The Borough
Dover
RAISZ

Sir Richard Steele
Courtesy of the National Portrait Gallery

Joseph Addison
Courtesy of the National Portrait Gallery

THE SIR ROGER DE COVERLEY PAPERS

FROM THE SPECTATOR

EDITED BY

H. G. PAUL, Ph.D.

PROFESSOR OF THE TEACHING OF ENGLISH
UNIVERSITY OF ILLINOIS

D. C. HEATH AND COMPANY

BOSTON NEW YORK CHICAGO
ATLANTA SAN FRANCISCO DALLAS
LONDON

4b7

Printed in the United States of America

PREFACE

Travelers in the realms of literature are soon charmed and fascinated by the days when Anne was Queen. To help the pupil re-live these days, to aid him in seeing how life then differed from ours, and yet how in many ways it was essentially like ours — such is the aim of this volume.

Provision has here been made for accommodating the amount and the nature of the study to the individual abilities and enthusiasms of the pupils. That the problems and projects here presented can evoke the sustained and fruitful efforts of students has been the pleasant experience of the editor with classes under his supervision in the University of Illinois High School. To the teachers and pupils in that school and to students in teachers' courses in literature in the University acknowledgment is gladly made for many helpful suggestions.

H. G. P.

CONTENTS

ILLUSTRATIONS

INTRODUCTION

London in the Days of "The Spectator."

Please imagine that we have seated ourselves on a magic wishing carpet and have quickly journeyed through time and space back to the days when Addison and Steele were publishing the *Spectator*. Let us step from our carpet to the dome of St. Paul's Cathedral, there on Ludgate Hill. This will be easier than climbing the six hundred steps of this great edifice, which was thirty-five years in building, and which was completed only a few months before the *Spectator* began to make its appearance.

From the dome we look down upon a city of nearly three-quarters of a million people, just about the population of Toronto or of Pittsburgh. Most of the metropolis is packed snugly along the north bank of the Thames, huddled so closely, in fact, that a walk of half an hour will take any citizen to those green fields which we see in the distance. Fortunately it is a clear, bright day, for frequently the fogs blot out the city, and in winter time a thick blanket of smoke often settles down and hides everything. This is before the days of smoke inspectors, and every ton of coal which is taxed to help pay for the building of St. Paul's is sending out its smoke and soot to discolor the fine new walls of the cathedral.

To the south of us stretches the Thames, crossed by a single bridge, which we as children have frequently celebrated in the verses about "London bridge is falling down."

Indeed when the old bridge rested on wooden piles, it was often menaced by the disaster suggested in our song, but now it is supported by thick stone arches so firm and strong that they can bear not only the weight of the bridge but also the broad shops and houses which flank its sides and make it resemble a busy city street. The river itself is alive with boats, for here is the great highway of travel from one part of the city to another. Below the bridge, extending as far as we can see, are the hundreds and hundreds of masts of those huge fleets of sailing vessels which make London the greatest and richest center of the world's commerce. At the south end of the bridge is a busy settlement, and the south bank of the Thames is thick with shops and homes; but farther back the land is marshy and comparatively uninhabited.

Turning now to the City proper, please look about a third of a mile below the bridge at those thick walls rising from the water's edge and flanked with turrets and towers. Hundreds of years ago, this Tower was a fort; then it became a residence for royalty and later a place of detention for political prisoners. You will be especially interested to know that Sir Walter Raleigh was confined there for twelve years, and that finally he was there beheaded. In the early eighteenth century the Tower is still noted as a prison — but only for animals. Some day we may go to see the lions in the Tower, for they are regarded as one of the great sights of London.

To the north of the Tower lies the Whitechapel district, the thickly crowded and not very attractive workingmen's quarters. There to the north of St. Paul's we can see the roofs of the Charterhouse, one of London's most famous schools, which both Addison and Steele attended before going to Oxford. Now please move to the west side of the dome. There in the foreground are the lawyers' quarters, extending from Gray's Inn, which with its gardens covers nearly thirty acres, on through Lincoln's Inn to the Middle and the Inner Temples with their grounds reaching down to the banks of the Thames. Note especially the Great Hall, the dining room of the Middle Temple. Here in the presence of Queen Elizabeth Shakespeare's *Twelfth Night* was performed a few years before Jamestown was settled. Not only are these Inns the center of the legal business of the nation, quarters in which the barristers have both their homes and their offices, but they are also the law schools of the land, for no one can be admitted to the practice of the law who has not kept the required number of terms as a student in one of these Inns. No wonder this is a big and busy section of London.

Next notice the street starting at our feet in front of St. Paul's and winding toward the west. Here it is called Ludgate Street, but every little while it changes its name. Farther on it becomes Fleet Street, and to the west of the lawyers' quarters it is the Strand. North of the Strand are crowded taverns and coffee-houses, theaters, and a great market. Our friend Dick Steele has called this region "the heart of the Town."

To the west and southwest are the houses of the aristocracy and of the royalty. Notice on the bank of the river the palace of White Hall, so close to the stream that the high waters sometimes invade the kitchen and put out the cooks' fires. History has been made here, for from one of its windows Charles I, sixty years before, stepped to the headsman's block, and in its banquet hall William and Mary were offered the crown a quarter of a century ago when her father, James II, had fled to France. Farther back we see royal parks and palaces, and in the distance rises Westminster Abbey, which we shall visit before long. Finally, take these good glasses and look up the river near its turn to the west. That is Vauxhall Gardens, which is the eighteenth century's nearest approach to our American Coney Island and White Cities. Perhaps we shall go there some night for supper and for the music.

Now that we have our bearings, let us descend and start on a tour of exploration. Be careful, for these long stairways are steep and not very well lighted. Then, too, see that your money and whatever other valuables you may have, including your handkerchiefs, are secure. We are going on a tremendously interesting trip, but one that involves many inconveniences and possibly a few dangers. So be prepared.

As we pass out of the Cathedral, we notice with surprise the costumes of the people we encounter. Most of the men are wearing three-cornered hats over wigs of various sizes and fashions. Here is a fellow in a great wig extending almost to his hips; at his side walks a friend, the end of whose wig is scarcely long enough to hold the ribbon with which it is bound.

Ordinary men, we soon perceive, wear black hats, sober-colored clothes, black stockings, and square-toed shoes with buckles. Their chief luxury is fine ruffled shirts imported from Holland; these are decidedly expensive. Men of higher station wear long, laced coats with cuffs "large enough to hold a gallon of wheat," and waistcoats that reach nearly to their knees. Around the neck is a large lace cravat, drawn through the buttonhole of the waistcoat. Look! there is a dandy in that sky-blue suit, the coat wired to make it stand out, his neck and wrists a mass of ruffles. From his buttonhole dangles an amber-headed cane; he carries a little muff, and at his side jangles a silver headed sword.

He is staring at that group of women; and indeed they are attractive in their riding hoods and long capes — reds and yellows and pinks, a veritable tulip bed. These women wear close-fitting bodices and skirts that are distended with hoops. Those shoes with the high red heels are the latest fashion. Indeed the chief object in life of these ladies is to follow the fashions; and they await impatiently each new importation of Parisian dolls dressed in the latest modes, for these models are the eighteenth-century forerunners of our own style shows. These ladies who are up to the minute in following the fashions, you notice, are each attended by a gaudily dressed little black boy carrying the curly lapdog and the fan.

Now we are ready to venture into the streets. How crooked and noisy and filthy they seem! Down the middle of the rough cobblestone pavement runs a broad gutter nearly choked with dirt and débris. Here and there the wheels of the coaches and carts have worn deep ruts through the pavement, and these places have been partly filled with faggots. Packhorses, coaches, and carts press forward, the drivers crowding and shouting and cursing till we are glad to take refuge behind the posts which at intervals protect the flagstone walk from the crush of the streets. "What are those strange boxes, slung between poles and each carried by two men?" you ask. Those are sedan chairs, a means of conveyance rapidly coming into fashion. These chairs, however, are not without their dangers, for yonder the bearers have squeezed a man against the wall. He wisely turns his back to escape the crash, but the passenger is deluged with a thousand bits of broken glass.

Walking the streets is no easy task, for the stone pavement is rough and irregular; shops jut into the streets; hogsheads of goods block the way; cellar doors lie open; and such wares as combs hung on strings dangle in our faces. At any moment we may be spattered by dirt flung from the wheels of coaches and carts. What a perfect bedlam of noises! Hawkers are vending everything from milk to doormats; scissors grinders ring their bells and blow their horns; and even the Fleet Street parson stands at his door, bawling for us to come in and be married! Hundreds of street signs swing and creak in the breeze, for in these times, when most men cannot read, they recognize these shops by such signs as the Blue Lyon, the Red Fox, the Purple Swan, the Golden Key, the Black Saracen. In the shop doors stand apprentices, who call lustily, "What do you lack? What do you lack?" If we stop to look in the shop windows, they may try to drag us in and to force us to buy. As we attempt to escape them, we may be surrounded by beggars, and Billie Lightfingers may try to relieve us of anything from a handkerchief to a watch. We are glad to turn into a quieter street in a better district, though even here the cries and annoyances are so great that, should they occur at home, we should hasten to call the police.

But look at what has happened to that sedan chair! It has been stopped by a constable! The bearers have opened up the chair, and the officer is serving a writ for debt on the dandy who is emerging. Notice carefully the details of his dress, as well as those of his sweetheart, who is offering her purse. That fellow on the right came from Wales; for it is St. David's Day, and like all other patriotic Welshmen, he observes the occasion by wearing a leek in his hat. But look out, or the lamp filler who has become absorbed in the scene below will spatter you with oil! Step aside for a moment to observe the houses down the street, since they will give you a very good idea of one of the better residence districts of London.

Perhaps you should like to sit down a few moments after our strenuous exercise; if so, let us go into one of the coffee-houses. Back in the mid-seventeenth century when coffee drinking and coffee-houses were novelties to the general run of Englishmen, many people agreed with the writer who railed at them, because men here "trifle away their time, scald their chops, and spend their money all for a little base, black, thick, nasty, bitter, nauseous puddle water." But despite such abuse the drinking of coffee gained rapidly in popularity, and now in the days of Anne more than three thousand coffee-houses are flourishing. Indeed we might well call this the age of the club and the coffee-house.

Notice, as we enter, the neatness of the place. The floor is covered with sand, and the tables are rubbed and polished

Hogarth's "The Arrest for Debt" (*Boston Public Library.*) See page xiv

HOGARTH'S "GAMBLING AT WHITE'S" (*Boston Public Library.*)

till we can almost see our faces in them. The walls are decorated with plate and with pictures, and in one corner blazes a cheery grate fire. At the desk sits a good-looking woman who manages the place, sees that the customers' wants are supplied, and collects the penny which is the customary fee for admission to the house. We aren't expecting any mail, of course, insomuch as our friends have to wait about two hundred years before they will be born, but it will be fun to ask her to look through the letters which are kept in the glass postal case.

Let us sit down, order a cup of coffee, and observe what is going on. Here are some young fellows, law students from the Temple, lounging in their dressing gowns with the strawberry-colored sashes, and watching a game of cards. Over in the corner two merchants are just concluding a sale of wine. That noisy crowd around the next table is discussing politics, while quite undisturbed by the uproar is a doctor prescribing for a patient, and a minister reading one of the newspapers which form a part of the equipment of the coffee-house.

A sharp-featured, alert-eyed man at the next table tells us that this place is Button's Coffee-house and that its proprietor has been a servant of the Countess of Warwick, whom the great Mr. Addison has been courting for many years. Formerly the wits and men of letters met at Will's, another near-by house, where Mr. Dryden, the poet and the critic, had his chair in the best corner near the fire in winter and near the window in summer. Here at Will's Addison, like the other young literary men of his time, had been delighted with a pinch of snuff from Dryden's box or with a kind word from the old poet who then ruled English literature. But despite the presence of these occasional kings of the coffee-houses, these resorts are essentially democratic. Every man is expected to talk to his neighbors, even if they are strangers. Most of these places observe a few simple and beneficial rules: thus, a man who swears is fined a shilling, and any one beginning a quarrel must treat each of the company to a "dish" of coffee.

Almost every coffee-house, continues our informant, is the haunt of some particular class of people. Thus, the Grecian is the resort of scholars; a duel was once fought there after a quarrel over the accent of a Greek word. Jonathan's and Garraway's are patronized by merchants, and Lloyd's by men interested in the shipping business. We do not tell our new-found friend that more than two hundred years later the coffee-house last named will have expanded into the world's most famous insurance company, but we think of the strange development which is destined to come. Impressed by the great interest in politics, we ask if members of the opposing parties frequent the same coffee-houses. "In many instances, yes; but there are exceptions. A Whig will no more go into the Cocoa Tree or Orzindas than a Tory will be seen in the coffee-house at St. James's."

As we are about to start out, refreshed and rested, we learn that our informant is Daniel Defoe, who is destined in that same coffee-house to meet a shipwrecked sailor and on that man's story to base the adventures of *Robinson Crusoe*. Before parting we ask him to direct us to an inn, and he suggests a famous one in the neighborhood where we may be sure of good food and of clean, comfortable quarters, and where we may observe the country folk and learn something of their ways of living. We thank him heartily and ask him to dine with us and are glad when he promptly accepts our invitation.

Leaving the coffee-house, let us enter one of the numerous churches whose tall spires stood out so prominently when we viewed the city from the dome of St. Paul's. Even if it is midweek, we shall probably find a congregation assembled, for in many of the churches services are held daily. The sermon is a very important part of the service, and often the minister does not hesitate to preach for even more than two hours. The music is not very impressive; half of the churches are without organs. Some of the people are really devout; some are there to ogle the beaux and belles; a few are asleep. The congregation is seated in square box pews, heavy with magnificent wood carvings. The preacher is cooped in a high pulpit. The wealthiest and more distinguished members have pews nearest the preacher; the lesser tradesmen are back of them; the poor are in the rear on benches or in the aisles. Finally the sermon is over and we are ready to leave; but we must not rush ahead of the chief people of the congregation, or they will think us rude. Here every one goes out in the order of his social importance. This is not our way, of course; but when we are in London, we must do as the Londoners do.

If you are well rested, let us start for the Queen's palace and for Westminster Abbey. As we go, perhaps we may well learn something about the English royalty of these days and of the political parties which are striving for power.

Queen Anne — good Queen Anne — has been on the throne for about ten years; she is the last sovereign of the House of Stuart, which has caused the nation so much trouble with the foolish doctrine of the divine right of kings to rule as they please. Her grandfather, Charles I, governed so arrogantly and so lawlessly that he brought on a civil war which cost him his throne and his head and sent his family, fearful for their lives, into exile in France. Then came the iron-handed government of the Puritans under the Lord Protector, Oliver Cromwell, a fierce, stern, strict old ruler, whose severity irked the people and made them ready after his death to call to the throne the exiled uncle of Queen Anne, Charles II. This king was an easy-going, dissolute man whose chief idea was that, happen whatever would, he had no intention of returning into exile in France. When he died in 1685, Anne's father, James II, ascended the throne, a pig-headed, obstinate man, a devout Roman

Catholic, and a firm believer in the divine right of kings. After tolerating his rule for three years, the nation rose, chased him into exile, and called to the throne his daughter Mary and her Dutch husband, William of Orange. After the death of William, which followed that of Mary by seven or eight years, her younger sister Anne was crowned in 1702. Exciting and trying years these have been, for the great Louis XIV of France has taken up the cause of Anne's exiled younger brother, and England has been drawn into the war flames of European politics. Fortunately the country then possessed one of the greatest generals of all history, the Duke of Marlborough, and his wonderful victories had shaken the power of France, which under the leadership of Louis XIV had come to dominate nearly the whole of western Europe. But, despite these successes, the war dragged along year after year, and we can hear at the coffee-houses that the Tories, for that is the name of the party in power, have begun to negotiate a peace.

This park of some eighty acres which we are now entering is called St. James's Park. Notice its long, straight canal and its rows of elms and lime trees. Yonder to the north is the fine palace which the nation has just built and presented to the Duke of Marlborough in gratitude for his victories. That long, rather low, rambling building to the west is St. James's Palace. Here Queen Anne was born and married, and this is the home she prefers to her other palaces at Kensington or at Hampton Court or out at Windsor. Do you see the red flag flying in front of the palace? That is raised only when the Queen is there. Sometimes she goes abroad to hunt, we are told; this she does in a chaise drawn by one horse, which she drives herself. Swift says that "she drives furiously like Jehu, and is a mighty hunter like Nimrod." Here she comes in her lumbering coach of state, a large, heavy, red-faced woman, a little past forty. Not a very keen or clever woman, we learn (she can be turned this way or that by her favorites), but a woman who has suffered much and is very devoted to the Church of England.

Life for her is made still harder by the intense party hatreds of her subjects. Of the two great political parties, the Whigs and the Tories, the Queen favors the latter, because she regards them as the staunch supporters of the Church of England. They are the conservatives, including many of the bishops of the church, some of the nobility, and nearly all the country gentlemen. They are the successors of the Cavaliers, who fought bravely but vainly for Anne's grandfather, Charles I. Their enemies, the Whigs, taunt them with leaning toward the Roman Catholic religion.

Queen Anne's position is made doubly difficult from the fact that while her heart is with the Tories, she is in no small measure indebted for her throne to the Whigs, who in 1688 had taken the lead in banishing her father. In her secret heart she wishes to have her young brother James, a Roman Catholic in exile in France, succeed her to the throne. But the Whigs are resolved to crown her second cousin, the Protestant George, Elector of Hanover. As the successors to the Roundheads, the Whigs are more favorable than are the Tories toward other Protestants not belonging to the Church of England, those Protestants who are called Dissenters. The strength of the Whigs lies among the nobility and especially among the manufacturing and trading classes of London, whose power and importance are increasing every year. Just at present the Tories are in power and are representing the Whigs as wishing to bring back the Commonwealth of the days of Cromwell.

The Palace of Westminster and the House of Lords, where Whig and Tory battle in Parliament, are only a short distance from the southeast entrance to St. James's Park, but at present we shall simply listen to the striking of Great Tom, there in the Parliament clock tower, and marvel a little as we learn that this clock has sounded the hour for hundreds of years. Perhaps we shall also recall that yonder

Westminster Hall has witnessed many strange reverses in the fortunes of kings and queens. Here Charles I was tried and condemned to be beheaded, and here, a half-century later, his granddaughter, Queen Anne, came for her coronation banquet.

But let us hasten to what many of us will regard as the most interesting place in all England — Westminster Abbey, a great church flanked with chapels and cloisters and halls and chambers. The church proper stretches the length of a full city block. As we enter, we notice that a hundred feet above us extends the carved wood work of its ceiling. The light comes to us soft and subdued through the colored glass of the leaded windows; yonder in the north transept of the church they are planning to restore the lovely rose-glass window, thirty-two feet in diameter. From time to time the church echoes with the deep notes of the lofty organ, blending with the voices of the minster choir.

Into this vast national shrine have been crowded for centuries and centuries the graves and the monuments of kings and queens, grand lords and their ladies, illustrious statesmen and famous warriors, eminent churchmen and distinguished writers — in a word, those whom the nation delighted to honor. Yonder in the poets' corner we discover the grave of Chaucer, with Dryden buried at his feet; and in this spot we know that Addison will some day rest. Here among the many chapels are two especially famous — that of Edward the Confessor, rich with its glowing marbles of many colors, and that of Henry VII. In these chapels have been buried the English sovereigns for century after century, and look! there stands the chair in which they were crowned. When Edward I returned from conquering Scotland in 1296, he brought with him the Fatal Stone of Scone on which the Scottish kings had been seated at their coronations, and he had it placed in the seat of an oaken chair. In that chair every successive king of England has been crowned. Notice also the newer chair built for Queen

Mary when she was crowned with her husband, William, in 1695.

We might easily and profitably spend the entire day inspecting this great museum of English national history, but perhaps we had better retrace our steps and seek an inn. We may, if we wish, take coaches or sedan chairs; but we shall find it cheaper and very interesting to descend the Westminster stairs to the Thames and there take a boat. The master boatman accommodates us by calling "Oars" if we wish a boat with two rowers, or by calling "Sculls" if we wish a boat with only one. The rates are cheap, being fixed by law; but we should find it even cheaper if we should take our places in one of those larger boats which might almost be called the river omnibusses. If it begins to rain, the oarsmen will raise above us a cloth supported by hoops, so that our boat resembles somewhat a covered wagon.

Our oarsmen row well and soon land us at the foot of the street leading to the inn where Defoe has promised to meet us. The inn itself proves to be a large, commodious place built with galleries around a court, which is filled with coaches and carts and wagons, coming and going, and resounding with what seems to us an intolerable din. The bedrooms are cold and drafty, but the beds are surrounded by heavy curtains, and above and below the lavender-scented sheets lie huge mattresses of feathers that would defy Jack Frost on the coldest night. We look at our huge watches, dangling on gay ribbons. It is almost four o'clock, the time all people of fashion are sitting down to dinner. After we have entered the dining room and have taken our places at the table, we ask Defoe to order for us a typical English dinner — which he does. Soon appears an immense piece of roast beef, flanked with cabbage and turnips, well salted and peppered, and swimming in butter. At other tables we see joints of mutton or pork, roast chicken and duck, rabbits and fish. Many of the company, we learn, are English squires up from the country for business rather than for pleasure. Red-faced and portly are most of them, and they wash down their huge dinners either with wine or, more frequently, with large and repeated draughts of ale or beer.

We learn from our friend, who seems to have been everywhere and to know everything that is doing, that just at present the roads are so deep with mud and mire that in many places travelers cannot make more than two miles an hour. Sometimes, under the strain, the heavy vehicles break down, or are overturned, or stick so fast that they are released only by the help of an added pair of strong oxen. Bridges are few and very poor; often they are entirely lacking, so that when the floods rise travelers must sometimes swim for their lives. If the wayfarer escapes these ills, he is subject to others. These are the days of highwaymen, who ply a brisk trade in relieving passengers of their money and their watches; they do not appear deterred in the least by the wayside gibbets which stand ready for men of their trade. Usually, in traveling, a guard, with his carbine across his knee, sits beside the coachman; but not infrequently coachman and guard and country landlord are all in league with the highwaymen. So we wonder that any of these country squires have ventured away from home.

When we ask our informant concerning the customs of these country squires, we learn that they live in houses of wood and plaster or of red brick, and that often the stables are disagreeably near the houses. Within the great living room are hung hams and flitches of bacon, together with guns and old swords, fishing tackle, powder horns, and stag horns. Perhaps we see lying on the high oak table a few worn books. The squire usually manages his own property, spends many hours in the saddle chasing the fox or hare, frequently attends a cockfight, and in the evening drinks long and deep with his boon companions at the tavern. On Sundays he sometimes goes to church and not infrequently sleeps through the sermon. His manners and his language are often coarse beyond description.

As the eldest son, he has inherited the family estate; in many instances he has consented that his brothers and sisters should live with him only on the condition that they rank as servants. His pride in his ancestry is immense; he glories in the portraits of his forebears; and he knows accurately his own family tree and that of each of his neighbors. His position as a squire gives him a place as an officer in the local militia, and in that office he glories as much as he does in his seat on the bench in the local courts. Indeed, if he is ambitious, he may come to represent the local shire in Parliament, and in London may join the October Club and there drink much ale and vow confusion and destruction to the Whigs. The staunchest of Tories, he hates foreigners and Dissenters, and his loyalty to the king is surpassed only by his loyalty to the church, not as a religious but as a great national institution. As for the unfortunate clergyman who lives in the squire's house and owes his appointment to that great man, his lot is hard and harsh. Often his wages are lower than those of many of the servants; he must leave the table when the dessert appears; and he may even be obliged to dig in the garden and to shoe the horses, while the squire talks loudly and drinks deeply as the champion of the church. Of course, we must remember through all this that Defoe is a Dissenter and sees the squires with the hostile eyes of a Whig.

But it is five o'clock; and unless we wish to send servants to the theater to hold places for us, we must prepare to go. Our choice of theaters can be made quickly, because there are only two or three playhouses. Perhaps we shall fare best if we go the the Theater Royal in Drury Lane, where Ambrose Philips's *The Distressed Mother* is to be performed. The author's good friends, Joseph Addison and Richard Steele, will be there. Indeed, Defoe informs us, Steele has undertaken to pack the house with his friends so that the play has every prospect of success. The price of admission is from one shilling to four. Two shillings secure a seat on the backless, green-covered benches just in front of the stage, in what is called the "pit." Around the sides of the pit are a semicircle of boxes, occupied mostly by the gentry. Above these rise two shallow galleries, the lower accommodating the plainer folk of the audience, and the upper being free to the footmen who have accompanied their masters. These footmen are a rough set, whistling, catcalling, and clattering with their sticks. Indeed they have grown to be such an intolerable nuisance that the managers are planning to exclude them from the theaters.

Hanging above the middle of the stage is a high, circular chandelier heavy with candles. It affords what the audience regards as excellent lighting of the theater, but one which to us, accustomed to electricity, seems decidedly dim and dusky. Notice that spectators have crowded into boxes on either side of the stage. One dandy is trying to attract the attention of the audience by standing up and waving his arms and calling to his friends in the pit.

The play is remarkably well received; for the players really please the audience, and Dick Steele and his friends are ready to applaud on any or no occasion. To us some features of the drama appear decidedly queer. For example, many of the players utter their lines in monotonous fashion, and some of them act as if they were delivering stump speeches. Then, too, we think it absurd for these supposedly noble Greeks and Trojans to be wearing the coats and dresses which a few months before had appeared in Queen Anne's court, for frequently the great lords and ladies passed on their finery to the actors. No one seems to see anything incongruous in Hector's widow parading the stage in a tight-fitting bodice and an immense hoop skirt.

At eight o'clock the play is over, and we mingle with the crowd in the dimly lighted street before the theater. Huge coaches dash up, threatening the very lives of the pedestrians; footmen bearing links run before the sedan chairs of the nobility and bawl, "Clear the way!" Thieves and pickpockets shuffle about, eager to ply their trade. Here and there gentlemen from the country are marshaling their armed servants, since all the Town is agog with stories concerning the fearful deeds of the Mohawks. These Mohawks are bands of young fellows about London, guilty of all kinds of mischief from breaking windows to gouging out eyes. Whether these gangs ever had any organization worthy of the name is extremely doubtful. But in these days when London is very inadequately policed, and when at night the streets are so dark and perilous that the wayfarer risks his money and even his life, these drunken young bloods find an exquisite pleasure and amusement in rolling people in barrels down steep and stony hills and in piercing with their swords the sides of sedan chairs. If the watchman interferes, he risks being beaten cruelly, having his nose slit, and possibly death. But our guide, Defoe, brings us in safety to Pontack's ordinary, the best and one of the most expensive of the restaurants in London, where we may hope to see Steele and Addison and their crowd come to celebrate the success of the evening's performance.

While we wait for their appearance, we remember that Defoe is a journalist and proceed to quiz him about the English newspapers. He tells us that during a larger part of the seventeenth century the government exercised a stringent censorship over the printing of news, especially of political news, and that even in the eighteenth century a publisher must be very careful or he will endanger his property and his body by offending the officials. Formerly information was broadcast through news-letters, which the editor wrote and then had duplicated on thin sheets by his assistants. Usually these news-letters filled only one side of the sheet, the back being reserved for news or business the purchaser might wish to include. Gradually it became customary to print these news-letters rather than to write them.

About the beginning of 1666 the government established its official paper, the *London Gazette;* this contained court notices and such foreign news as the ruling political party wished printed and was usually very dull. The editorship has been a political prize; in April, 1708, it was given to Dick Steele, but he was too ardent a Whig, and in October, 1710, he lost this post on account of his offensive partisanship.

The chief of the newspapers, Defoe goes on to tell us, is the *Postman*, which appears on Tuesdays, Thursdays, and Saturdays, and is so famous that it is known all over Europe. Its editor, a French Protestant named Fonvive, is said to clear from it more than six hundred pounds a year. The first daily newspaper, Defoe continues, was the *Daily Courant*, which made its bow to the public just three days after Anne was crowned in 1702. "I remember that the first issue consisted of ten short items, translations from newspapers in Amsterdam and Paris. For a long time I doubted whether it could survive, but now it has fallen into the hands of Samuel Buckley, who publishes the *Spectator*. He is an excellent printer and a splendid business man, especially in the matter of getting advertisements; so I believe that the *Courant* will prosper."

Here one of our company remembers that Defoe himself is publishing a paper and asks about it. "There isn't much to be said concerning the *Review*," comes the answer, "except that it is fairly prosperous. Now and then I get into trouble, for I have never dodged a good fight. Perhaps you will be interested to know that some people suspect that Dick Steele borrowed a number of ideas for his *Tatler* and *Spectator* from my Scandal Club, a club which helped the circulation of the *Review* enormously. But Dick's papers have caught the favor of the town and draw more trade to the coffee-houses than all the other papers which may there be read."

Here we are interrupted by the bustle and stir caused by the arrival of Ambrose Philips, the author of the play we saw at the theater, accompanied by his friends Steele and Addison and a few others. Philips is in a jovial and prodigal mood, for wasn't tonight's performance the third night of the play, that night when the proceeds all fall to the share of the author? And weren't those receipts a fine and handsome sum? No wonder he is anxious to treat the friends who had packed the house. Steele is in high spirits and is the life of the party; no one would suspect that the bailiffs are after him for what he owes on that rich red velvet suit he is wearing and for the fine sword that dangles at his side. His broad, dark face is flushed with excitement and with wine. Addison is pale and reserved — some of us think him a trifle haughty, — but gradually the good food and the excellent wine quicken him to talk; then the rest of the company are silent and listen till he ceases. Soon Dick Steele, who has been seated beside him, leads a round of applause.

But Great Tom, the London clock, is saying that it is midnight; our charm will soon lose its power; and so we step upon our magic carpet. In a moment even the tall dome of St. Paul's, standing there upon Ludgate Hill, vanishes from our sight. Soon we are rubbing our eyes back in twentieth-century America. We are glad to be home, but tomorrow we shall be pleased to know what two centuries have learned about Addison and Steele and the place they are holding among the enduring writers of our language.

Richard Steele and Joseph Addison.

Richard Steele (1662–1729) was, in his own words, "an Englishman born in the city of Dublin." His early school days were spent at the famous Charterhouse in London, whence he went to Oxford; but instead of working for his degree, he threw aside his books and enlisted as a soldier. Then, growing tired of this life in a red coat, he exchanged the sword for the pen and was by turns a political pamphleteer and a dramatist. Finally he started a newspaper. Steele was always busy with some new scheme, always seeking the pot of gold at the end of the rainbow, almost always in debt. He spent his money like a lord and borrowed from one friend to pay another; and his broad, dark face and thick-set figure were as familiar to the bailiffs with their judgments for debts as to his friends and cronies at the coffee-houses. Warm-hearted, generous, impulsive, sinning and repenting, good-natured Dick Steele passes before us. Now he is sending his wife, his "dearest Prue," a love note which encloses two guineas, some tea, or "twenty-nine walnuts"; now he is rising in Parliament to oppose an unjust measure brought forward by his own party, the Whigs, though he knows that his speech will cost him his seat. Such a package of contradictions was Richard Steele!

He early realized his shortcomings; so to force himself to live nearer to his ideals, he published his *Christian Hero*, 1701, in which he urged that men should practice what they preach. Then, because his fellow officers laughed at his book as the "dull work of a dull fellow," he strove to "enliven his character" and to raise the tone of the stage by producing three clean, bright plays: *The Funeral*, 1702; *The Lying Lover*, 1703; and *The Tender Husband*, 1705. These plays mark the beginning of sentimental comedy.

In April, 1709, Steele "opened a vein of the finest literary gold" in the essays of his tri-weekly journal, the *Tatler*. Before long Addison came to his assistance, and together they raised the *Tatler* in fame and favor; but in 1710 they brought it to a close to begin the better-conceived and ultimately more popular *Spectator*. This, in turn, was followed by the *Guardian* in 1714; but the call of his party was then ringing in Steele's ears, so the new venture gradually took on a partisan tone. A little later the accession of George I brought the Whigs back to power, and Dick Steele then became Sir Richard and a member of Parliament. During the following years of his checkered career he assailed his political foes in several short-lived journals and brought out his most successful play, *The Conscious Lovers*, 1722. Finally he left London for his wife's home in Wales, where, broken in health and fortune, he died in 1729.

Far more pleasant was the life of Addison which began, about six weeks after Steele's, at his father's rectory in the little village of Milson in Wiltshire. His friendship with Steele was formed at the Charterhouse School and was continued at Oxford, where Addison proved much the better scholar and wrote some excellent Latin verses which are scarcely inferior to Milton's. Soon the kindly and aging Dryden welcomed him to the circle at Will's Coffee-house in London; and Congreve introduced him to the Whig ministers of state, who granted him a pension that he might travel on the Continent and prepare himself for a political position. Four years later, Addison returned to England, skilled in the French language and broadened by his travels in western Europe. But at the death of King William in 1702 the Whigs were driven from office, and consequently his pension was stopped. Fortune, however, soon came to his relief. In 1704 the ministry was seeking a poet who could celebrate fittingly Marlborough's triumph at Blenheim; and we see, with wonder, a powerful and haughty chancellor of the exchequer climbing a poet's narrow stairs to ask his aid. Addison capped his verses, *The Campaign*, with some lines likening the undaunted Marlborough directing the battle to a calm angel directing the whirlwind. The simile swept the Town and brought its author a profitable office. In the next twelve years Addison rose from place to place, becoming a member of Parliament and finally secretary of state.

His literary fame grew apace with his political success. From 1709 to 1712 he aided Steele in writing the *Tatler* and the *Spectator;* and in 1713 he drew another large prize in the lottery of literature with his tragedy *Cato*. We of today, however, would gladly exchange this lumbering play for a few more of his *Hymns*, such as "The spacious firmament on high," and "The Lord my pastures shall prepare." During his later years he gathered around him a little circle of admirers and held sway at Button's Coffee-house much as Dryden had done at Will's. He passed away peacefully in 1719 and was buried in Westminster Abbey.

Addison and Steele are now remembered chiefly by their essays in the *Tatler* and the *Spectator*. Most of these essays filled practically an entire issue of the journal, which was printed on a single page of coarse paper about twice as long and not quite twice as wide as the page of an ordinary text-book. The *Tatler*, which sold for a penny, appeared on the regular post days — Tuesday, Thursday, and Saturday; it was discontinued with No. 271 about the beginning of 1711. Steele was known as the responsible editor of both the *Tatler* and the *Spectator* and contributed to the former about four times as many papers as did his colleague. Of the five hundred fifty-five issues of the *Spectator*, which appeared each week day, Addison's share was slightly the larger.

"Whatever is of human interest," quotes Steele, "shall be our theme"; and as we turn the pages of the *Tatler* and the *Spectator* we realize how apt are his words. In one number we get a glimpse of Steele's childhood as he stands beating his father's coffin and calling his dead parent; in another we discover Addison's eulogy of the old ballad "Chevy Chase." Here are his famous criticisms of *Paradise Lost*, and his satire on Signor Nicolini, the popular tenor at the opera, fighting the tailor who is dressed as a lion. We smile as we read of the dissection of a beau's head or a belle's heart, the one as empty as the other is cold; or we laugh at the transmigration of the soul of Pugg the monkey. Now the essayist is playfully scolding his readers for following the extreme fashions; now he is warning them against wasting their time.

Nowhere could such a variety of subjects better come up for discussion than at the club which Steele and Addison formed for carrying on the work of the *Spectator*. Consider how typical of the great interests of those days are the members of that imaginary group. Will Honeycomb, the gay gallant, represents the Wits of the Restoration; and the Whig, Sir Andrew Freeport, is a representative of the growing class of merchants. Then comes the clergyman and next the Templar — one of that new species, the critic, — and next the Spectator himself, who with his taciturn interest in the life about him strongly suggests Addison. Best of all is that staunch old Tory, the country squire Sir Roger de Coverley. We are glad to turn again to such passages as the account of his siege of the obdurate widow's heart, his waking up from a nap in church and rising to reprove one of his tenants for nodding there, and his visit to the playhouse and to Westminster Abbey. The quaint and kindly Sir Roger holds a sure place among the immortals of literature.

When we attempt to summarize what Steele and Addison accomplished for English literature, we recognize, in the first place, that, like Chaucer and Bunyan and Pepys, they have left us a unique picture of the life of their times:

"As we read the delightful volumes of the *Tatler* and *Spectator*," says Thackeray, "the past age returns, the England of our ancestors is revivified. The Maypole rises in the Strand again in London; the churches are thronged with daily worshipers; the beaux are going into the coffee-houses; the gentry are going to the drawing room; the ladies are thronging the toy-shops; the chairmen are jostling in the streets; the footmen are running with links before the chariots or fighting round the theatre doors."

Again, we can scarcely overestimate the value of the *Tatler* and the *Spectator* in civilizing England, in raising the standard of morals and manners. They purified and sweetened the wit of the profligate sons of the Cavaliers and brought a smile to the somber faces of the sons of the Puritans. Their earnest protests and good-natured satire worked wonders in creating a cleaner and kindlier public sentiment and in recommending "Truth, Innocence, Honor, and Virtue as the chief ornaments of life."

Moreover, they aided in the development of letters by gradually enlarging the reading public and thus helping to lessen the dependence of authors upon their patrons, the wealthy nobles. Steele and Addison were the first to appeal especially to their women readers, and many of our great grandmothers struggled through the alphabet that they might learn to read these delightful papers. Furthermore, these Autocrats of the Eighteenth-Century Breakfast Table aided in the development of the essay by giving it more of the tone of the better talk of better people; and in the depicting of Sir Roger they almost quickened the character sketch into the novel. Finally, Addison especially worked wonders in improving the style of English prose. He strove for simplicity that he might reach all classes of his readers, and he cultivated a passion for perfect expression that often led him to stop the printing press to change a conjunction or a preposition.

Into the quarrel of the critics concerning the relative merits of Addison and Steele we need not enter. If Steele was the warmer-hearted and the more generous, Addison was the more consistent and lived the better life. If Steele was the quicker and keener in invention, Addison was the more skillful in rounding and perfecting these conceptions. In their union lay their strength; and the *Tatler* and the *Spectator* stand as an enduring monument to their friendship.

SIR ROGER DE COVERLEY PAPERS FROM THE SPECTATOR.

THE SPECTATOR'S ACCOUNT OF HIMSELF.

[ADDISON.]

NO. 1.—THURSDAY, MARCH 1, 1710–11.

NON fumum ex fulgore, sed ex fumo dare lucem
Cogitat, ut speciosa dehinc miracula promat.
—HOR. ARS POET. ver. 143.

ONE with a flash begins, and ends in smoke;
Another out of smoke brings glorious light,
And (without raising expectation high)
Surprises us with dazzling miracles.—ROSCOMMON.

I HAVE observed that a reader seldom peruses a book with pleasure, till he knows whether the writer of it be a black or a fair man, of a mild or choleric disposition, married or a bachelor, with other particulars of the like nature, that conduce very much to the right understanding of an author. To gratify this curiosity, which is so natural to a reader, I design this paper, and my next, as prefatory discourses to my following writings, and shall give some account in them of the several persons that are engaged in this work. As the chief trouble of compiling, digesting, and correcting, will fall to my share, I must do myself the justice to open the work with my own history.

I was born to a small hereditary estate, which, according to the tradition of the village where it lies, was bounded by the same hedges and ditches in William the Conqueror's time that it is at present, and has been delivered down from father to son whole and entire, without the loss or acquisition of a single field or meadow, during the space of six hundred years. There runs a story in the family, that my mother, near the time of my birth, dreamed that her son was become a judge; whether this might proceed from a law-suit which was then depending in the family, or my father's being a justice of the peace, I cannot determine; for I am not so vain as to think it presaged any dignity that I should arrive at in my future life, though that was the interpretation which the neighbourhood put upon it. The gravity of my behaviour at my very first appearance in the world seemed to favour my mother's dream: for as she often told me, I threw away my rattle before I was two months old, and would not make use of my coral until they had taken away the bells from it.

As for the rest of my infancy, there being nothing in it remarkable, I shall pass it over in silence. I find, that during my nonage, I had the reputation of a very sullen youth, but was always a favourite of my schoolmaster, who used to say, that my parts were solid, and would wear well. I had not been long at the university, before I distinguished myself by a most profound silence; for, during the space of eight years, excepting in the public exercises of the college, I scarce uttered the quantity of an hundred words; and indeed do not remember that I ever spoke three sentences together in my whole life. Whilst I was in this learned body, I applied myself with so much diligence to my studies, that there are very few celebrated books, either in the learned or the modern tongues, which I am not acquainted with.

Upon the death of my father, I was resolved to travel into foreign countries, and therefore left the university, with the character of an odd unaccountable fellow, that had a great deal of learning, if I would but shew it. An insatiable thirst after knowledge carried me into all the countries of Europe, in which there was anything new or strange to be seen; nay, to such a degree was my curiosity raised, that having read the controversies of some great men concerning the antiquities of Egypt, I made a voyage to Grand Cairo, on purpose to take the measure of a pyramid; and as soon as I had set myself right in that particular, returned to my native country with great satisfaction.

I have passed my latter years in this city, where I am frequently seen in most public places, though there are not above half-a-dozen of my select friends that know me; of whom my next paper shall give a more particular account. There is no place of general resort, wherein I do not often make my appearance: sometimes I am seen thrusting my head into a round of politicians, at Will's, and listening with great attention to the narratives that are made in those little circular audiences. Sometimes I smoke a pipe at Child's, and whilst I seem attentive to nothing but the Postman, overhear the conversation of every table in the room. I appear on Sunday nights at St. James's coffee house, and sometimes join the little committee of politics in the inner room, as one who comes there to hear and improve. My face is likewise very well known at the Grecian, the Cocoa-tree, and in the theatres both of Drury-Lane and the Hay-market. I have been taken for a merchant upon the exchange for above these ten years, and sometimes pass for a Jew in the assembly of stock-jobbers at Jonathan's: in short, wherever I see a cluster of people, I always mix with them, though I never open my lips but in my own club.

Thus I live in the world rather as a spectator of mankind, than as one of the species, by which means I have made myself a speculative statesman, soldier, merchant, and artisan, without ever meddling with any practical part in life. I am very well versed in the theory of a husband or a father, and can discern the errors in the economy, business, and diversion of others, better than those who are engaged in them; as standers-by discover blots, which are apt to escape those who are in the game. I never espoused any party with violence, and am resolved to observe an exact neutrality between the Whigs and Tories, unless I shall be forced to declare myself by the hostilities of either side. In short, I have acted in all the parts of my life as a looker-on, which is the character I intend to preserve in this paper.

I have given the reader just so much of my history and character, as to let him see I am not altogether unqualified for the business I have undertaken. As for other particulars in my life and adventures, I shall insert them in following papers, as I shall see occasion. In the meantime, when I consider how much I have seen, read, and heard, I begin to blame my own taciturnity; and since I have neither time nor inclination, to communicate the fulness of my heart in speech, I am resolved to do it in writing, and to print myself out, if possible, before I die. I have been often told by my friends, that it is a pity so many useful discoveries which I have made should be in the possession of a silent man. For this reason, therefore, I shall publish a sheet-full of thoughts every morning, for the benefit of my contemporaries: and if I can any way contribute to the diversion or improvement of the country in which I live, I shall leave it when I am summoned out of it, with the secret satisfaction of thinking that I have not lived in vain.

There are three very material points which I have not spoken to in this paper; and which, for several important reasons, I must keep to myself, at least for some time: I mean, an account of my name, my age, and my lodgings. I must confess, I would gratify my reader in anything that is reasonable; but as for these three particulars, though I am sensible they might tend very much to the embellishment of my paper, I cannot yet come to a resolution of communicating them to the public. They would indeed draw me out of that obscurity which I have enjoyed for many years, and expose me in public places to several salutes and civilities, which have been always very disagreeable to me; for the greatest pain I can suffer, is the being talked to, and being stared at. It is for this reason likewise, that I keep my complexion and dress as very great secrets; though it is not impossible that I may make discoveries of both in the progress of the work I have undertaken.

After having been thus particular upon myself, I shall,

in to-morrow's paper, give an account of those gentlemen who are concerned with me in this work; for, as I have before intimated, a plan of it is laid and concerted, as all other matters of importance are, in a club. However, as my friends have engaged me to stand in the front, those who have a mind to correspond with me may direct their letters to the Spectator, at Mr. Buckley's in Little Britain. For I must further acquaint the reader, that, though our club meet, only on Tuesdays and Thursdays, we have appointed a committee to sit every night, for the inspection of all such papers as may contribute to the advancement of the public weal.

C.

THE SPECTATOR'S CLUB. [STEELE.]

No. 2. — FRIDAY, MARCH 2, 1710–11.

AST alii sex
Et plures uno conclamant ore. — JUV. SAT. vii. 167.

SIX more at least join their consenting voice.

THE first of our society is a gentleman of Worcestershire, of ancient descent, a baronet, his name is Sir Roger de Coverley. His great grandfather was inventor of that famous country-dance which is called after him. All who know that shire are very well acquainted with the parts and merits of Sir Roger. He is a gentleman that is very singular in his behaviour, but his singularities proceed from his good sense, and are contradictions to the manners of the world, only as he thinks the world is in the wrong. However, this humour creates him no enemies, for he does nothing with sourness or obstinacy; and his being unconfined to modes and forms, makes him but the readier and more capable to please and oblige all who know him. When he is in town, he lives in Soho Square. It is said, he keeps himself a bachelor, by reason he was crossed in love by a perverse beautiful widow of the next county to him. Before this disappointment, Sir Roger was what you call a fine gentleman, had often supped with my Lord Rochester and Sir George Etherege, fought a duel upon his first coming to town, and kicked Bully Dawson in a public coffee house for calling him youngster. But, being ill used by the above mentioned widow, he was very serious for a year and a half; and though, his temper being naturally jovial, he at last got over it, he grew careless of himself, and never dressed afterwards. He continues to wear a coat and doublet of the same cut, that were in fashion at the time of his repulse, which, in his merry humours, he tells us, has been in and out twelve times since he first wore it. He is now in his fifty-sixth year, cheerful, gay, and hearty; keeps a good house both in town and country; a great lover of mankind: but there is such a mirthful cast in his behaviour, that he is rather beloved than esteemed. His tenants grow rich, his servants look satisfied, all the young women profess love to him, and the young men are glad of his company; when he comes into a house, he calls the servants by their names, and talks all the way up stairs to a visit. I must not omit, that Sir Roger is a justice of the *quorum;* that he fills the chair at a quarter-sessions with great abilities, and three months ago, gained universal applause, by explaining a passage in the game-act.

The gentleman next in esteem and authority among us, is another bachelor, who is a member of the Inner Temple; a man of great probity, wit, and understanding; but he has chosen his place of residence rather to obey the direction of an old humoursome father, than in pursuit of his own inclinations. He was placed there to study the laws of the land, and is the most learned of any of the house in those of the stage. Aristotle and

Longinus are much better understood by him than Littleton or Coke. The father sends up every post questions relating to marriage articles, leases and tenures, in the neighbourhood; all which questions he agrees with an attorney to answer and take care of in the lump. He is studying the passions themselves, when he should be inquiring into the debates among men which arise from them. He knows the argument of each of the orations of Demosthenes and Tully; but not one case in the reports of our own courts. No one ever took him for a fool, but none, except his intimate friends, know he has a great deal of wit. This turn makes him at once both disinterested and agreeable; as few of his thoughts are drawn from business, they are most of them fit for conversation. His taste of books is a little too just for the age he lives in; he has read all, but approves of very few. His familiarity with the customs, manners, actions, and writings of the ancients, makes him a very delicate observer of what occurs to him in the present world. He is an excellent critic, and the time of the play is his hour of business; exactly at five he passes through New Inn, crosses through Russell court, and takes a turn at Will's, till the play begins; he has his shoes rubbed, and his periwig powdered at the barber's as you go into the Rose. It is for the good of the audience when he is at a play; for the actors have an ambition to please him.

The person of next consideration is Sir Andrew Freeport, a merchant of great eminence in the city of London. A person of indefatigable industry, strong reason, and great experience. His notions of trade are noble and generous, and (as every rich man has usually some sly way of jesting, which would make no great figure were he not a rich man) he calls the sea the British Common. He is acquainted with commerce in all its parts, and will tell you that it is a stupid and barbarous way to extend dominion by arms, for true power is to be got by arts and industry. He will often argue, that if this part of our trade were well cultivated, we should gain from one nation, — and if another, from another. I have heard him prove, that diligence makes more lasting acquisitions than valour, and that sloth has ruined more nations than the sword. He abounds in several frugal maxims, amongst which the greatest favourite is, 'A penny saved is a penny got.' A general trader of good sense is pleasanter company than a general scholar; and Sir Andrew having a natural unaffected eloquence, the perspicuity of his discourse gives the same pleasure that wit would in another man. He has made his fortunes himself; and says that England may be richer than other kingdoms, by as plain methods as he himself is richer than other men; though at the same time I can say this of him, that there is not a point in the compass but blows home a ship in which he is an owner.

Next to Sir Andrew in the club-room sits Captain Sentry, a gentleman of great courage, good understanding, but invincible modesty. He is one of those that deserve very well, but are very awkward at putting their talents within the observation of such as should take notice of them. He was some years a captain, and behaved himself with great gallantry in several engagements and at several sieges; but having a small estate of his own, and being next heir to Sir Roger, he has quitted a way of life, in which no man can rise suitably to his merit, who is not something of a courtier as well as a soldier. I have heard him often lament, that in a profession where merit is placed in so conspicuous a view, impudence should get the better of modesty. When he has talked to this purpose, I never heard him make a sour expression, but frankly confess that he left the world, because he was not fit for it. A strict honesty and an even regular behaviour are in themselves obstacles to him that must press through crowds who endeavour at the same end with himself, the favour of a commander. He will, however, in his way of talk, excuse generals for not disposing according to men's desert, or inquiring into it: for, says he, that great man who has a mind to help me, has as many to break through to come at me, as I have to come at him: therefore, he will conclude, that the man who would make a figure, especially in a military way, must get over all false modesty, and assist his patron against the importunity of other pretenders, by a proper assurance in his own vindication. He says, it is a civil cowardice to be backward in asserting what you ought to expect, as it is a military fear to be slow in attacking when it is your duty. With this candor does the gentleman speak of himself and others. The same frankness runs through all his conversation. The military part of his life has furnished him with many adventures, in the relation of which he is very agreeable to the company; for he is never over-bearing, though accustomed to command men in the utmost degree below him; nor ever too obsequious, from an habit of obeying men highly above him.

But, that our society may not appear a set of humourists, unacquainted with the gallantries and pleasures of the age, we have among us the gallant Will Honeycomb, a gentleman who, according to his years, should be in the decline of his life, but, having ever been very careful of his person, and always had a very easy fortune, time has made but a very little impression, either by wrinkles on his forehead, or traces on his brain. His person is well turned, of a good height. He is very ready at that sort of discourse with which men usually entertain women. He has all his life dressed very well, and remembers habits as others do men. He can smile when one speaks to him, and laughs easily. He knows the history of every mode, and can inform you from what Frenchwoman our wives and daughters had this manner of curling their hair, that way of placing their hoods; and whose vanity to shew her foot made that part of the dress so short in such a year. In a word, all his conversation and knowledge have been in the female world; as other men of his age will take notice to you what such a minister said upon such and such an occasion, he will tell you, when the Duke of Monmouth danced at court, such a woman was then smitten, another was taken with him at the head of his troop in the Park. For all these important relations, he has ever about the same time received a kind glance or a blow of a fan from some celebrated beauty, mother of the present Lord such-a-one.

This way of talking of his very much enlivens the conversation, among us of a more sedate turn; and I find there is not one of the company, but myself, who rarely speak at all, but speaks of him as of that sort of man who is usually called a well-bred fine gentleman. To conclude his character, where women are not concerned, he is an honest worthy man.

I cannot tell whether I am to account him whom I am next to speak of, as one of our company; for he visits us but seldom, but when he does, it adds to every man else a new enjoyment of himself. He is a clergyman, a very philosophic man, of general learning, great sanctity of life, and the most exact good breeding. He has the misfortune to be of a very weak constitution; and consequently cannot accept of such cares and business as preferments in his function would oblige him to; he is therefore among divines what a chamber-councillor is among lawyers. The probity of his mind, and the integrity of his life, create him followers, as being eloquent or loud advances others. He seldom introduces the subject he speaks upon; but we are so far gone in years that he observes, when he is among us, an earnestness to have him fall on some divine topic, which he always treats with much authority, as one who has no interest in this world, as one who is hastening to the object of all his wishes, and conceives hope from his decays and infirmities. These are my ordinary companions. R.

SIR ROGER ON MEN OF FINE PARTS. [STEELE.]

No. 6. — WEDNESDAY, MARCH 17, 1710–11.

CREDEBANT hoc grande nefas, et morte piandum,
Si juvenis vetulo non assurrexerat. — JUV. SAT. xiii. 54.

'TWAS impious then (so much was age rever'd)
For youth to keep their seats when an old man appear'd.

I KNOW no evil under the sun so great as the abuse of the understanding, and yet there is no one vice more common. It has diffused itself through both sexes, and all qualities of mankind; and there is hardly that person to be found, who is not more concerned for the reputation of wit and sense, than honesty and virtue. But this unhappy affectation of being wise rather than honest, witty than good-natured, is the source of most of the ill habits of life. Such false impressions are owing to the abandoned writings of men of wit, and the awkward imitation of the rest of mankind.

For this reason, Sir Roger was saying last night, that he was of opinion that none but men of fine parts deserve to be hanged. The reflections of such men are so delicate upon all occurrences which they are concerned in, that they should be exposed to more than ordinary infamy and punishment, for offending against such quick admonitions as their own souls give them, and blunting the fine edge of their minds in such a manner, that they are no more shocked at vice and folly, than men of slower capacities. There is no greater monster in being, than a very ill man of great parts. He lives like a man in a palsy, with one side of him dead. While perhaps he enjoys the satisfaction of luxury, of wealth, of ambition, he has lost the taste of good will, of friendship, of innocence. Scarecrow, the beggar in Lincoln's-inn-fields, who disabled himself in his right leg, and asks alms all day to get himself a warm supper at night, is not half so despicable a wretch, as such a man of sense. The beggar has no relish above sensations; he finds rest more agreeable than motion; and while he has a warm fire, never reflects that he deserves to be whipped. Every man who terminates his satisfactions and enjoyments within the supply of his own necessities and passions is, says Sir Roger, in my eye as poor a rogue as Scarecrow. "But," continued he, "for the loss of public and private virtue we are beholden to your men of fine parts forsooth; it is with them no matter what is done, so it be done with an air. But to me who am so whimsical in a corrupt age as to act according to nature and reason, a selfish man in the most shining circumstance and equipage, appears in the same condition with the fellow above mentioned, but more contemptible in proportion to what more he robs the public of and enjoys above him. I lay it down therefore for a rule, that the whole man is to move together; that every action of any importance, is to have a prospect of public good: and that the general tendency of our indifferent actions ought to be agreeable to the dictates of reason, of religion, of good breeding; without this, a man, as I have before hinted, is hopping instead of walking, he is not in his entire and proper motion."

While the honest knight was thus bewildering himself in good starts, I looked intentively upon him, which made him, I thought, collect his mind a little. "What I aim at," says he, "is, to represent, that I am of opinion, to polish our understandings and neglect our manners is of all things the most inexcusable. Reason should govern passion, but instead of that, you see, it is often subservient to it; and, as unaccountable as one would think it, a wise man is not always a good man." This degeneracy is not only the guilt of particular persons, but also at some times of a whole people: and perhaps it may appear upon examination, that the most polite ages are the least virtuous. This may be attributed to the folly of admitting wit and learning as merit in themselves, without considering the application of them. By this means it becomes a rule, not so much to regard what we do, as how we do it. But this false beauty will not pass upon men of honest minds and true taste. Sir Richard Blackmore says, with as much good sense as virtue, "It is a mighty dishonour and shame to employ excellent faculties and abundance of wit, to humour and please men in their vices and follies. The great enemy of mankind, notwithstanding his wit and angelic faculties, is the most odious being in the whole creation." He goes on soon after to say, very generously, that he undertook the writing of his poem "to rescue the Muses out of the hands of ravishers, to restore them to their sweet and chaste mansions, and to engage them in an employment suitable to their dignity." This certainly ought to be the purpose of every man who appears in public, and whoever does not proceed upon that foundation, injures his country as fast as he succeeds in his studies. When modesty ceases to be the chief ornament of one sex, and integrity of the other, society is upon a wrong basis, and we shall be ever after without rules to guide our judgment in what is really becoming and ornamental. Nature and reason direct one thing, passion and humour another. To follow the dictates of these two latter, is going into a road that is both endless and intricate; when we pursue the other, our passage is delightful, and what we aim at easily attainable.

I do not doubt but England is at present as polite a nation as any in the world; but any man who thinks can easily see, that the affectation of being gay and in fashion, has very near eaten up our good sense and our religion. Is there anything so just as that mode and gallantry should be built upon exerting ourselves in what is proper and agreeable to the institutions of justice and piety among us? And yet is there anything more common, than that we run in perfect contradiction to them? All which is supported by no other pretension, than that it is done with what we call a good grace.

Nothing ought to be held laudable or becoming, but what nature itself should prompt us to think so. Respect to all kinds of superiors is founded, methinks, upon instinct; and yet what is so ridiculous as age? I make this abrupt transition to the mention of this vice, more than any other, in order to introduce a little story, which I think a pretty instance that the most polite age is in danger of being the most vicious.

"It happened at Athens, during a public representation of some play exhibited in honour of the commonwealth, that an old gentleman came too late for a place suitable to his age and quality. Many of the young gentlemen, who observed the difficulty and confusion he was in, made signs to him that they would accommodate him if he came where they sat. The good man bustled through the crowd accordingly; but when he came to the seats to which he was invited, the jest was to sit close and expose him, as he stood out of countenance, to the whole audience. The frolic went round all the Athenian benches. But on those occasions there were also particular places assigned for foreigners. When the good man skulked towards the boxes appointed for the Lacedæmonians, that honest people, more virtuous than polite, rose up all to a man, and with the greatest respect received him among them. The Athenians being suddenly touched with a sense of the Spartan virtue and their own degeneracy, gave a thunder of applause; and the old man cried out, 'The Athenians understand what is good, but the Lacedæmonians practise it.'"

R.

THE SPECTATOR AT HIS CLUB. [ADDISON.]

No. 34.—MONDAY, APRIL 9, 1711.

—parcit
Cognatis maculis similis fera.—JUV. SAT. xv. 159.

FROM spotted skins the leopard does refrain.—TATE.

THE club of which I am a member, is very luckily composed of such persons as are engaged in different ways of life, and deputed as it were out of the most conspicuous classes of mankind: by this means I am furnished with the greatest variety of hints and materials, and know everything that passes in the different quarters and divisions, not only of this great city, but of the whole kingdom. My readers too have the satisfaction to find that there is no rank or degree among them who have not their representative in this club, and that there is always somebody present who will take care of their respective interests, that nothing may be written or published to the prejudice or infringement of their just rights and privileges.

I last night sate very late in company with this select body of friends, who entertained me with several remarks which they and others had made upon these my speculations, as also with the various success which they had met with among their several ranks and degrees of readers. Will Honeycomb told me, in the softest manner he could, that there were some ladies (but for your comfort, says Will, they are not those of the most wit) that were offended at the liberties I had taken with the opera and the puppet-show; that some of them were likewise very much surprised that I should think such serious points as the dress and equipage of persons of quality, proper subjects for raillery.

He was going on, when Sir Andrew Freeport took him up short, and told him, that the papers he hinted at had done great good in the city, and that all their wives and daughters were the better for them; and further added, that the whole city thought themselves very much obliged to me for declaring my generous intentions to scourge vice and folly as they appear in a multitude, without condescending to be a publisher of particular intrigues. "In short," says Sir Andrew, "if you avoid that foolish beaten road of falling upon aldermen and citizens, and employ your pen upon the vanity and luxury of courts, your paper must needs be of general use."

Upon this my friend the Templar told Sir Andrew that he wondered to hear a man of his sense talk after that manner; that the city had always been the province for satire; and that the wits of King Charles's time jested upon nothing else during his whole reign. He then shewed, by the examples of Horace, Juvenal, Boileau, and the best writers of every age, that the follies of the stage and court had never been accounted too sacred for ridicule, how great soever the persons might be that patronised them. "But after all," says he, "I think your raillery has made too great an excursion in attacking several persons of the Inns of Court; and I do not believe you can shew me any precedent for your behaviour in that particular."

My good friend Sir Roger de Coverley, who had said nothing all this while, began his speech with a pish! and told us that he wondered to see so many men of sense so very serious upon fooleries. "Let our good friend," says he, "attack every one that deserves it: I would only advise you, Mr. Spectator," applying himself to me, "to take care how you meddle with country squires: they are the ornaments of the English nation; men of good heads and sound bodies! and let me tell you, some of them take it ill of you that you mention fox-hunters with so little respect."

Captain Sentry spoke very sparingly on this occasion. What he said was only to commend my prudence in not touching upon the army, and advised me to continue to act discreetly in that point.

By this time I found every subject of my speculations was taken away from me by one or other of the club; and began to think myself in the condition of the good man that had one wife who took a dislike to his grey hairs, and another to his black, till by their picking out what each of them had an aversion to, they left his head altogether bald and naked.

While I was thus musing with myself, my worthy friend the clergyman, who, very luckily for me, was at the club that night, undertook my cause. He told us that he wondered any order of persons should think themselves too considerable to be advised: that it was not quality, but innocence, which exempted men from reproof: that vice and folly ought to be attacked wherever they could be met with, and especially when they were placed in high and conspicuous stations of life. He further added, that my paper would only serve to aggravate the pains of poverty, if it chiefly exposed those who are already depressed, and in some measure turned into ridicule, by the meanness of their conditions and circumstances. He afterwards proceeded to take notice of the great use this paper might be of to the public, by reprehending those vices which are too trivial for the chastisement of the law, and too fantastical for the cognisance of the pulpit. He then advised me to prosecute my undertaking with cheerfulness, and assured me, that whoever might be displeased with me, I should be approved by all those whose praises do honour to the persons on whom they are bestowed.

The whole club pays a particular deference to the discourse of this gentleman, and are drawn into what he says as much by the candid ingenuous manner with which he delivers himself, as by the strength of argument and force of reason which he makes use of. Will Honeycomb immediately agreed, that what he had said was right; and that, for his part, he would not insist upon the quarter which he had demanded for the ladies. Sir Andrew gave up the city with the same frankness. The Templar would not stand out; and was followed by Sir Roger and the Captain; who all agreed that I should be at liberty to carry the war into what quarter I pleased; provided I continued to combat with criminals in a body, and to assault the vice without hurting the person.

This debate which was held for the good of mankind, put me in mind of that which the Roman triumvirate were formerly engaged in for their destruction. Every man at first stood hard for his friend, till they found that by this means they should spoil their proscription: and at last making a sacrifice of all their acquaintance and relations, furnished out a very decent execution.

Having thus taken by resolutions, to march out boldly in the cause of virtue and good sense, and to annoy their adversaries in whatever degree or rank of men they may be found, I shall be deaf for the future to all the remonstrances that shall be made to me on this account. If Punch grows extravagant, I shall reprimand him very freely: if the stage becomes a nursery of folly and impertinence, I shall not be afraid to animadvert upon it. In short, if I meet with anything in city, court, or country, that shocks modesty or good manners, I shall use my utmost endeavours to make an example of it. I must however intreat every particular person who does me the honour to be a reader of this paper, never to think himself, or any of his friends or enemies, aimed at in what is said: for I promise him, never to draw a faulty character which does not fit at least a thousand people: or to publish a single paper, that is not written in the spirit of benevolence, and with a love to mankind.

C.

SIR ROGER AT HOME. [ADDISON.]

NO. 106. — MONDAY, JULY 2, 1711.

HINC tibi copia
Manabit ad plenum, benigno
Ruris honorum opulenta cornu.
— HOR. LIB. I. OD. xvii. 14.

HERE plenty's liberal horn shall pour
Of fruits for thee a copious show'r,
Rich honours of the quiet plain.

HAVING often received an invitation from my friend Sir Roger de Coverley to pass away a month with him in the country, I last week accompanied him thither, and am settled with him for some time at his country-house, where I intend to form several of my ensuing speculations. Sir Roger, who is very well acquainted with my humour, lets me rise and go to bed when I please; dine at his own table or in my chamber, as I think fit, sit still and say nothing without bidding me be merry. When the gentlemen of the country come to see him, he only shews me at a distance: as I have been walking in his fields I have observed them stealing a sight of me over an hedge, and have heard the knight desiring them not let me see them, for that I hated to be stared at.

I am the more at ease in Sir Roger's family, because it consists of sober and staid persons: for as the knight is the best master in the world, he seldom changes his servants; and as he is beloved by all about him, his servants never care for leaving him; by this means his domestics are all in years, and grown old with their master. You would take his Valet-de-chambre for his brother, his butler is grey-headed, his groom is one of the gravest men that I have ever seen, and his coachman has the looks of a privy-counsellor. You see the goodness of the master even in the old house-dog, and in a grey pad that is kept in the stable with great care and tenderness out of regard to his past services, though he has been useless for several years.

I could not but observe with a great deal of pleasure the joy that appeared in the countenance of these ancient domestics upon my friend's arrival at his country-seat. Some of them could not refrain from tears at the sight of their old master; every one of them pressed forward to do something for him, and seemed discouraged if they were not employed. At the same time the good old knight, with a mixture of the father and the master of the family, tempered the inquiries after his own affairs with several kind questions relating to themselves. This humanity and good nature engages everybody to him, so that when he is pleasant upon any of them, all his family are in good humour, and none so much as the person whom he diverts himself with: on the contrary, if he coughs, or betrays any infirmity of old age, it is easy for a stander by to observe a secret concern in the looks of all his servants.

My worthy friend has put me under the particular care of his butler, who is a very prudent man, and, as well as the rest of his fellow-servants, wonderfully desirous of pleasing me, because they have often heard their master talk of me as of his particular friend.

My chief companion, when Sir Roger is diverting himself in the woods or the fields, is a very venerable man who is ever with Sir Roger, and has lived at his house in the nature of a chaplain above thirty years. This gentleman is a person of good sense and some learning, of a very regular life and obliging conversation: he heartily loves Sir Roger, and knows that he is very much in the old knight's esteem, so that he lives in the family rather as a relation than a dependant.

I have observed in several of my papers that my friend Sir Roger, amidst all his good qualities, is something of an humourist; and that his virtues, as well as imperfections, are, as it were, tinged by a certain extravagance, which makes them particularly his, and distinguishes them from those of other men. This cast of mind, as it is generally very innocent in itself, so it renders his conversation highly agreeable, and more delightful than the same degree of sense and virtue would appear in their common or ordinary colours. As I was walking with him last night, he asked me how I liked the good man whom I have just now mentioned; and, without staying for my answer, told me that he was afraid of being insulted with Latin and Greek at his own table; for which reason he desired a particular friend of his at the university to find him out a clergyman rather of plain sense than much learning, of a good aspect, a clear voice, a sociable temper: and, if possible, a man that understood a little of back-gammon. "My friend," says

Sir Roger, "found me out this gentleman, who, besides the endowments required of him, is, they tell me, a good scholar, though he does not shew it: I have given him the parsonage of the parish; and because I know his value, have settled upon him a good annuity for life. If he outlives me, he shall find that he was higher in my esteem than perhaps he thinks he is. He has now been with me thirty years; and though he does not know I have taken notice of it, has never in all that time asked any thing of me for himself, though he is every day soliciting me for something in behalf of one or other of my tenants, his parishioners. There has not been a law-suit in the parish since he has lived among them; if any dispute arises they apply themselves to him for the decision; if they do not acquiesce in his judgment, which I think never happened above once or twice at most, they appeal to me. At his first settling with me, I made him a present of all the good sermons which have been printed in English, and only begged of him that every Sunday he would pronounce one of them in the pulpit. Accordingly, he has digested them into such a series, that they follow one another naturally, and make a continued system of practical divinity."

As Sir Roger was going on in his story, the gentleman we were talking of came up to us; and upon the knight's asking him who preached to-morrow (for it was Saturday night) told us the Bishop of St. Asaph in the morning, and Dr. South in the afternoon. He then shewed us his list of preachers for the whole year, where I saw with a great deal of pleasure Archbishop Tillotson, Bishop Saunderson, Dr. Barrow, Dr. Calamy, with several living authors who have published discourses of practical divinity. I no sooner saw this venerable man in the pulpit, but I very much approved of my friend's insisting upon the qualifications of a good aspect and a clear voice; for I was so charmed with the gracefulness of his figure and delivery, as well as with the discourses he pronounced, that I think I never passed any time more to my satisfaction. A sermon repeated after this manner, is like the composition of a poet in the mouth of a graceful actor.

I could heartily wish that more of our country clergy would follow this example; and instead of wasting their spirits in laborious compositions of their own, would endeavour after a handsome elocution, and all those other talents that are proper to enforce what has been penned by greater masters. This would not only be more easy to themselves, but more edifying to the people.

L.

THE COVERLEY HOUSEHOLD. [STEELE.]

NO. 107.—TUESDAY, JULY 3, 1711.

ÆSOPO ingentem statuam posuere Attici,
Servumque collocarunt æterna in basi,
Patere honoris scirent ut cunctis viam.—PHÆDR. EP. I. 2.

THE Athenians erected a large statue to Æsop, and placed him, through a slave, on a lasting pedestal; to shew, that the way to honour lies open indifferently to all.

THE reception, manner of attendance, undisturbed freedom and quiet, which I meet with here in the country, has confirmed me in the opinion I always had, that the general corruption of manners in servants is owing to the conduct of masters. The aspect of every one in the family carries so much satisfaction, that it appears he knows the happy lot which has befallen him in being a member of it. There is one particular which I have seldom seen but at Sir Roger's; it is usual in all other places, that servants fly from the parts of the house through which their master is passing; on the contrary, here they industriously place themselves in his way; and it is on both sides, as it were, understood as a visit, when the servants appear without calling. This proceeds from the humane and equal temper of the man of the house, who also perfectly well knows how to enjoy a great estate with such economy as ever to be much beforehand. This makes his own mind untroubled, and consequently unapt to vent peevish expressions, or give passionate or inconsistent orders to those about him. Thus respect and love go together; and a certain cheerfulness in performance of their duty is the particular distinction of the lower part of this family. When a servant is called before his master, he does not come with an expectation to hear himself rated for some trivial fault, threatened to be stripped, or used with any other unbecoming language, which mean masters often give to worthy servants; but it is often to know, what road he took that he came so readily back according to order; whether he passed by such a ground; if the old man who rents it is in good health; or whether he gave Sir Roger's love to him, or the like.

A man who preserves a respect founded on his benevolence to his dependants, lives rather like a prince than a master in his family: his orders are received as favors rather than duties; and the distinction of approaching him is part of the reward for executing what is commanded by him.

There is another circumstance in which my friend excels in his management, which is the manner of rewarding his servants. He has ever been of opinion, that giving his cast clothes to be worn by valets has a very ill effect upon little minds, and creates a silly sense of equality between the parties, in persons affected only with outward things. I have heard him often pleasant on this occasion, and describe a young gentleman abusing his man in that coat, which a month or two before was the most pleasing distinction he was conscious of in himself. He would turn his discourse still more pleasantly upon the ladies' bounties of this kind; and I have heard him say he knew a fine woman, who distributed rewards and punishments in giving becoming or unbecoming dresses to her maids.

But my good friend is above these little instances of good-will, in bestowing only trifles on his servants: a good servant to him is sure of having it in his choice very soon of being no servant at all. As I before observed, he is so good a husband, and knows so thoroughly that the skill of the purse is the cardinal virtue of this life; I say he knows so well that frugality is the support of generosity, that he can often spare a large fine when a tenement falls, and give that settlement to a good servant who has a mind to go into the world, or make a stranger pay the fine to that servant for his more comfortable maintenance, if he stays in his service.

A man of honor and generosity considers it would be miserable to himself to have no will but that of another, though it were of the best person breathing, and for that reason, goes on as fast as he is able to put his servants into independent livelihoods. The greatest part of Sir Roger's estate is tenanted by persons who have served himself or his ancestors. It was to me extremely pleasant to observe the visitants from several parts to welcome his arrival into the country; and all the difference that I could take notice of between the late servants who came to see him, and those who stayed in the family was, that these latter were looked upon as finer gentlemen and better courtiers.

This manumission and placing them in a way of livelihood, I look upon as only what is due to a good servant; which encouragement will make his successor be as diligent, as humble, and as ready as he was. There is something wonderful in the narrowness of those minds which can be pleased, and be barren of bounty to those who please them.

One might, on this occasion, recount the sense that great persons in all ages have had of the merit of their dependants, and the heroic services which men have done their masters in the extremity of their fortunes, and shewn to their undone patrons that fortune was all the difference between them; but as I design this my speculation only as a gentle admonition to thankless masters, I shall not go out of the occurrences of common life, but assert it as a general observation, that I never saw, but in Sir Roger's family and one or two more, good servants treated as they ought to be. Sir Roger's kindness extends to their children's children; and this very morning he sent his coachman's grandson to prentice. I shall conclude this paper with an account of a picture in his gallery, where there are many which will deserve my future observation.

At the very upper end of this handsome structure I saw the portraiture of two young men standing in a river, the one naked, the other in a livery. The person supported seemed half dead, but still so much alive as to shew in his face exquisite joy and love towards the other. I thought the fainting figure resembled my friend Sir Roger; and looking at the butler who stood by me, for an account of it, he informed me that the person in the livery was a servant of Sir Roger's, who stood on the shore while his master was swimming, and observing him taken with some sudden illness and sink under water, jumped in and saved him. He told me Sir Roger took off the dress he was in as soon as he came home, and by a great bounty at that time, followed by his favour ever since, had made him master of that pretty seat which we saw at a distance as we came to this house. I remembered, indeed, Sir Roger said, there lived a very worthy gentleman, to whom he was highly obliged, without mentioning any thing farther. Upon my looking a little dissatisfied at some part of the picture, my attendant informed me that it was against Sir Roger's will, and at the earnest request of the gentleman himself, that he was drawn in the habit in which he had saved his master. R.

WILL WIMBLE. [ADDISON.]

NO. 108. — WEDNESDAY, JULY 4, 1711.

GRATIS anhelans multa agendo nihil agens.

— PHÆDR. FAB. V. l. 2.

OUT of breath to no purpose, and very busy about nothing.

As I was yesterday morning walking with Sir Roger before his house, a country fellow brought him a huge fish, which he told him Mr. Will Wimble had caught that morning; and that he presented it with his service to him, and intended to come and dine with him. At the same time he delivered a letter, which my friend read to me as soon as the messenger left him.

"SIR ROGER, — I desire you to accept of a jack, which is the best I have caught this season. I intend to come and stay with you a week, and see how the perch bite in the Black River. I observed with some concern, the last time I saw you upon the bowling-green, that your whip wanted a lash to it; I will bring half a dozen with me that I twisted last week, which I hope will serve you all the time you are in the country. I have not been out of the saddle for six days past, having been at Eaton with Sir John's eldest son. He takes to his learning hugely. — I am, Sir, your humble servant,

WILL WIMBLE."

This extraordinary letter, and message that accompanied it, made me very curious to know the character and quality of the gentleman who sent them; which I found to be as follows. Will Wimble is younger brother to a baronet, and descended of the ancient family of the Wimbles. He is now between forty and fifty: but being bred to no business, and born to no estate, he generally lives with his elder brother as superintendent of his game. He hunts a pack of dogs better than any man in the country, and is very famous for finding out a hare. He is extremely well versed in all the little handicrafts of an idle man: he makes a May-fly to a miracle; and furnishes the whole country with angle rods. As he is a good-natured officious fellow, and very much esteemed upon account of his family, he is a welcome guest at every house, and keeps up a good correspondence among all the gentlemen about him. He carries a tulip-root in his pocket from one to another, or exchanges a puppy between a couple of friends that live perhaps in the opposite sides of the county. Will is a particular favourite of all the young heirs, whom he frequently obliges with a net that he has weaved, or a setting dog that he has made himself. He now and then presents a pair of garters of his own knitting to their mothers or sisters; and raises a great deal of mirth among them by inquiring as often as he meets them, how they wear? These gentleman-like manufactures and obliging little humours make Will the darling of the country.

Sir Roger was proceeding in the character of him, when we saw him make up to us with two or three hazel twigs in his hand that he had cut in Sir Roger's woods, as he came through them in his way to the house. I was very much pleased to observe, on one side the hearty and sincere welcome with which Sir Roger received him, and on the other the secret joy which his guest discovered at sight of the good old knight. After the first salutes were over, Will desired Sir Roger to lend him one of his servants to carry a set of shuttle-cocks he had with him in a little box to a lady that lived about a mile off, to whom it seems he had promised such a present for above this half year. Sir Roger's back was no sooner turned but honest Will began to tell me of a large cock-pheasant that he had sprung in one of the neighbouring woods, with two or three other adventures of the same nature. Odd and uncommon characters are the game that I look for, and most delight in; for which reason I was as much pleased with the novelty of the person that talked with me, as he could be for his life with the springing of a pheasant, and therefore listened to him with more than ordinary attention.

In the midst of his discourse the bell rung to dinner, where the gentleman I have been speaking of had the pleasure of seeing the huge jack he had caught, served up for the first dish in a most sumptuous manner. Upon our sitting down to it, he gave us a long account how he had hooked it, played with it, foiled it, and at length drew it out upon the bank, with several other particulars that lasted all the first course. A dish of wild fowl that came afterwards furnished conversation for the rest of the dinner, which concluded with a late invention of Will's for improving the quail-pipe.

Upon withdrawing into my room after dinner, I was secretly touched with compassion towards the honest gentleman that had dined with us; and could not but consider with a great deal of concern, how so good a heart and such busy hands were wholly employed in trifles; that so much humanity should be so little beneficial to others, and so much industry so little advantageous to himself. The same temper of mind and application to affairs might have recommended him to the public esteem, and might have raised his fortune in another station of life. What good to his country or himself might not a trader or a merchant have done with such useful though ordinary qualifications!

Will Wimble's is the case of many a younger brother of a great family, who had rather see their children starve like gentlemen, than thrive in a trade or profession that is beneath their quality. This humour fills several parts of Europe with pride and beggary. It is the happiness of a trading nation like ours, that the younger sons, though incapable of any liberal art or profession, may be placed in such a way of life as may perhaps enable them to vie with the best of their family: accordingly we find several citizens that were launched into the world with narrow fortunes, rising by honest industry to greater estates than those of their elder brothers. It is not improbable but Will was formerly tried at divinity, law, or physic; and that, finding his genius did not lie that way, his parents at length gave him up to his own inventions. But certainly, however improper he might have been for studies of a higher nature, he was perfectly well turned for the occupations of trade and commerce. As I think this a point which cannot be too much inculcated, I shall desire my reader to compare what I have here written with what I have said in my twenty-first speculation.

L.

THE COVERLEY PORTRAITS. [STEELE.]

NO. 109.—THURSDAY, JULY 5, 1711.

ABNORMIS sapiens.—HOR. LIB. 2. SAT. ii. 3.

OF plain good sense, untutor'd in the schools.

I WAS this morning walking in the gallery, when Sir Roger entered at the end opposite to me, and advancing towards me, said he was glad to meet me among his relations the De Coverleys, and hoped I liked the conversation of so much good company, who were as silent as myself. I knew he alluded to the pictures, and as he is a gentleman who does not a little value himself upon his ancient descent, I expected he would give me some account of them. We were now arrived at the upper end of the gallery, when the knight faced towards one of the pictures, and as we stood before it, he entered into the matter after his blunt way of saying things as they occur to his imagination, without regular introduction, or care to preserve the appearance of a chain of thought.

"It is," said he, "worth while to consider the force of dress; and how the persons of one age differ from those of another, merely by that only. One may observe also, that the general fashion of one age has been followed by one particular set of people in another, and by them preserved from one generation to another. Thus the vast jetting coat and small bonnet, which was the habit in Henry the Seventh's time, is kept on in the yeoman of the guard; not without a good and politic view, because they look a foot taller, and a foot and a half broader — besides that the cap leaves the face expanded, and consequently more terrible and fitter to stand at the entrance of palaces.

"This predecessor of ours, you see, is dressed after this manner, and his cheeks would be no larger than mine were he in a hat as I am. He was the last man that won a prize in the Tiltyard (which is now a common street before Whitehall). You see the broken lance that lies there by his right foot. He shivered that lance of his adversary all to pieces; and bearing himself, look you, Sir, in this manner, at the same time he came within the target of the gentleman who rode against him, and taking him with incredible force before him on the pummel of his saddle, he in that manner rid the tournament over, with an air that shewed he did it rather to perform the rules of the lists, than expose his enemy: however, it appeared he knew how to make use of a victory, and with a gentle trot he marched up to a gallery where their mistress sat (for they were rivals), and let him down with laudable courtesy and pardonable insolence. I do not know but it might be exactly where the coffee-house is now.

"You are to know this my ancestor was not only a military genius, but fit also for the arts of peace, for he played on the bass-viol as well as any gentleman at court; you see where his viol hangs by his basket-hilt sword. The action at the Tiltyard, you may be sure, won the fair lady, who was a maid of honour and the greatest beauty of her time; here she stands, the next picture. You see, Sir, my great great great grandmother has on the new-fashioned petticoat, except that the modern is gathered at the waist; my grandmother appears as if she stood in a large drum, whereas the ladies now walk as if they were in a go-cart. For all this lady was bred at court, she became an excellent country-wife, she brought ten children, and when I shew you the library, you shall see in her own hand (allowing for the difference of the language) the best receipt now in England both for a hasty-pudding and a white-pot.

"If you please to fall back a little, because it is necessary to look at the three next pictures at one view; these are three sisters. She on the right hand who is so very beautiful, died a maid; the next to her, still handsomer, had the same fate, against her will; this homely thing in the middle had both their portions added to her own, and was stolen by a neighbouring gentleman, a man of stratagem and resolution; for he poisoned three mastiffs to come at her, and knocked down two deer-stealers in carrying her off. Misfortunes happen in all families. The theft of this romp, and so much money, was no great matter to our estate. But the next heir that possessed it was this soft gentleman whom you see there. Observe the small buttons, the little boots, the laces, the slashes about his clothes, and above all the posture he is drawn in (which to be sure was his own choosing): you see he sits with one hand on a desk, writing, and looking as it were another way, like an easy writer, or a sonneteer. He was one of those that had too much wit to know how to live in the world; he was a man of no justice, but great good manners; he ruined anybody that had any thing to do with him, but never said a rude thing in his life; the most indolent person in the world, he would sign a deed that passed away half his estate with his gloves on, but would not put on his hat before a lady if it were to save his country. He is said to be the first that made love by squeezing the hand. He left the estate with ten thousand pounds debt upon it; but, however, by all hands I have been informed, that he was every way the finest gentleman in the world. That debt lay heavy on our house for one generation, but it was retrieved by a gift from that honest man you see there, a citizen of our name, but nothing at all akin to us. I know Sir Andrew Freeport has said behind my back, that this man was descended from one of the ten children of the maid of honour I shewed you above: but it was never made out. We winked at the thing indeed, because money was wanting at that time."

Here I saw my friend a little embarrassed, and turned my face to the next portraiture.

Sir Roger went on with his account of the gallery in the following manner: "This man (pointing to him I looked at) I take to be the honour of our house, Sir Humphrey de Coverley; he was in his dealings as punctual as a tradesman, and as generous as a gentleman. He would have thought himself as much undone by breaking his word, as if it were to be followed by bankruptcy. He served his country as a knight of the shire to his dying day. He found it no easy matter to maintain an integrity in his words and actions, even in things that regarded the offices which were incumbent upon him, in the care of his own affairs and relations of life, and therefore dreaded (though he had great talents) to go into employments of state, where he must be exposed to the snares of ambition. Innocence of life, and great ability, were the distinguishing parts of his character; the latter, he had often observed, had led to the destruction of the former, and he used frequently to lament that great and good had not the same signification. He was an excellent husbandman, but had resolved not to exceed such a degree of wealth; all above it he bestowed in secret bounties many years after the sum he aimed at for his own use was attained. Yet he did not slacken his industry, but to a decent old age spent the life and fortune which were superfluous to himself, in the service of his friends and neighbours."

Here we were called to dinner, and Sir Roger ended the discourse of this gentleman, by telling me, as we followed the servant, that this his ancestor was a brave man, and narrowly escaped being killed in the civil wars; "for," said he, "he was sent out of the field upon a private message, the day before the battle of Worcester." The whim of narrowly escaping by having been within a day of danger, with other matters abovementioned, mixed with good sense, left me at a loss whether I was more delighted with my friend's wisdom or simplicity. R.

THE COVERLEY GHOST. [ADDISON.]

NO. 110.—FRIDAY, JULY 6, 1711.

HORROR ubique animos, simul ipsa silentia terrent.
—VIRG. ÆN. ii. 755.

ALL things are full of horror and affright,
And dreadful e'en the silence of the night.—DRYDEN.

AT a little distance from Sir Roger's house, among the ruins of an old abbey, there is a long walk of aged elms; which are shot up so very high, that when one passes under them, the rooks and crows that rest upon the tops of them, seem to be cawing in another region. I am very much delighted with this sort of noise, which I consider as a kind of natural prayer to that Being who supplies the wants of his whole creation, and who, in the beautiful language of the Psalms, feedeth the young ravens that call upon him. I like this retirement the better, because of an ill report it lies under of being haunted; for which reason, as I have been told in the family, no living creature ever walks in it besides the chaplain. My good friend the butler desired me, with a very grave face, not to venture myself in it after sunset, for that one of the footmen had been almost frightened out of his wits by a spirit that appeared to him in the shape of a black horse without an head; to which he added, that about a month ago, one of the maids coming home late that way, with a pail of milk upon her head, heard such a rustling among the bushes, that she let it fall.

I was taking a walk in this place last night between the hours of nine and ten, and could not but fancy it one of the most proper scenes in the world for a ghost to appear in. The ruins of the abbey are scattered up and down on every side, and half covered with ivy and elder bushes, the harbours of several solitary birds, which seldom make their appearance till the dusk of the evening. The place was formerly a churchyard, and has still several marks in it of graves and burying-places. There is such an echo among the old ruins and vaults, that if you stamp but a little louder than ordinary, you hear the sound repeated. At the same time the walk of elms, with the croaking of the ravens, which from time to time are heard from the tops of them, looks exceeding solemn and venerable. These objects naturally raise seriousness and attention; and when night heightens the awfulness of the place, and pours out her supernumerary horrors upon every thing in it, I do not at all wonder that weak minds fill it with spectres and apparitions.

Mr. Locke, in his chapter of the association of ideas, has very curious remarks, to shew how, by the prejudice of education, one idea often introduces into the mind a whole set that bear no resemblance to one another in the nature of things. Among several examples of this kind, he produces the following instance. *The ideas of goblins and sprights have really no more to do with darkness than light; yet let but a foolish maid inculcate these often on the mind of a child, and raise them there together, possibly he shall never be able to separate them again so long as he lives; but darkness shall ever afterwards bring with it those frightful ideas, and they shall be so joined, that he can no more bear the one than the other.*

As I was walking in this solitude, where the dusk of the evening conspired with so many other occasions of terror, I observed a cow grazing not far from me, which an imagination that was apt to startle might easily have construed into a black horse without an head: and I dare say the poor footman lost his wits upon some such trivial occasion.

My friend Sir Roger has often told me, with a great deal of mirth, that at his first coming to his estate, he found three parts of his house altogether useless; that the best room in it had the reputation of being haunted, and by that means was locked up; that noises had been heard in his long gallery, so that he could not get a servant to enter it after eight o'clock at night; that the door of one of his chambers was nailed up, because there went a story in the family that a butler had formerly hanged himself in it; and that his mother, who lived to a great age, had shut up half the rooms in the house, in which either her husband, a son, or daughter had died. The knight seeing his habitation reduced to so small a compass, and himself in a manner shut out of his own house, upon the death of his mother, ordered all the apartments to be flung open, and exorcised by his chaplain, who lay in every room one after another, and by that means dissipated the fears which had so long reigned in the family.

I should not have been thus particular upon these ridiculous horrors, did not I find them so very much prevail in all parts of the country. At the same time I think a person who is thus terrified with the imagination of ghosts and spectres much more reasonable than one who, contrary to the reports of all historians sacred and profane, ancient and modern, and to the traditions of all nations, thinks the appearance of spirits fabulous and groundless. Could not I give myself up to this general testimony of mankind, I should to the relations of particular persons who are now living, and whom I cannot distrust in other matters of fact. I might here add, that not only the historians, to whom we may join the poets, but likewise the philosophers of antiquity, have favoured this opinion. Lucretius himself, though by the course of his philosophy he was obliged to maintain that the soul did not exist separate from the body, makes no doubt of the reality of apparitions, and that men have often appeared after their death. This I think very remarkable; he was so pressed with the matter of fact, which he could not have the confidence to deny, that he was forced to account for it by one of the most absurd unphilosophical notions that was ever started. He tells us, that the surfaces of all bodies are perpetually flying off from their respective bodies, one after another; and that these surfaces or thin cases that included each other whilst they were joined in the body like the coats of an onion, are sometimes seen entire when they are separated from it; by which means we often behold the shapes and shadows of persons who are either dead or absent.

L.

THE CORONATION CHAIR (*Publishers Photo Service.*)

St. Clement's Danes

Built just a little later than the time of Sir Roger, to fill a great demand for new churches in the growing city. (*Photo by Ewing Galloway.*)

SUNDAY AT COVERLEY HALL. [ADDISON.]

NO. 112. — MONDAY, JULY 9, 1711.

'Αθανάτους μὲν πρῶτα θεούς, νόμῳ ὡς διάκειται,
Τίμα —— — PYTHAG.

FIRST, in obedience to thy country's rites,
Worship th' immortal gods.

I AM always very well pleased with a country Sunday, and think, if keeping holy the seventh day were only a human institution, it would be the best method that could have been thought of for the polishing and civilizing of mankind. It is certain the country people would soon degenerate into a kind of savages and barbarians, were there not such frequent returns of a stated time in which the whole village meet together with their best faces, and in their cleanliest habits, to converse with one another upon indifferent subjects, hear their duties explained to them, and join together in adoration of the Supreme Being. Sunday clears away the rust of the whole week, not only as it refreshes in their minds the notions of religion, but as it puts both the sexes upon appearing in their most agreeable forms, and exerting all such qualities as are apt to give them a figure in the eye of the village. A country fellow distinguishes himself as much in the churchyard, as a citizen does upon the Change, the whole parish-politics being generally discussed in that place either after sermon or before the bell rings.

My friend Sir Roger, being a good churchman, has beautified the inside of his church with several texts of his own chusing: he has likewise given a handsome pulpit-cloth, and railed in the communion table at his own expence. He has often told me, that at his coming to his estate he found his parishioners very irregular; and that in order to make them kneel and join in the responses, he gave every one of them a hassoc and a common-prayer book: and at the same time employed an itinerant singing master, who goes about the country for that purpose, to instruct them rightly in the tunes of the psalms; upon which they now very much value themselves, and indeed outdo most of the country churches that I have ever heard.

As Sir Roger is landlord to the whole congregation, he keeps them in very good order, and will suffer nobody to sleep in it besides himself; for if by chance he has been surprised into a short nap at sermon, upon recovering out of it he stands up and looks about him, and if he sees anybody else nodding, either wakes them himself, or sends his servants to them. Several other of the old knight's particularities break out upon these occasions: sometimes he will be lengthening out a verse in the singing-psalms, half a minute after the rest of the congregation have done with it; sometimes, when he is pleased with the matter of his devotion, he pronounces *Amen* three or four times to the same prayer; and sometimes stands up when everybody else is upon their knees, to count the congregation, or see if any of his tenants are missing.

I was yesterday very much surprised to hear my old friend, in the midst of the service, calling out to one John Matthews to mind what he was about, and not disturb the congregation. This John Matthews it seems is remarkable for being an idle fellow, and at that time was kicking his heels for his diversion. This authority of the knight, though exerted in that odd manner which accompanies him in all circumstances of life, has a very good effect upon the parish, who are not polite enough to see any thing ridiculous in his behaviour; besides that the general good sense and worthiness of his character makes his friends observe these little singularities as foils that rather set off than blemish his good qualities.

As soon as the sermon is finished, nobody presumes to stir till Sir Roger is gone out of the church. The knight walks down from his seat in the chancel between a double row of his tenants, that stand bowing to him on each side; and every now and then inquires how such a one's wife, or mother, or son, or father do, whom he does not see at church; which is understood as a secret reprimand to the person that is absent.

The chaplain has often told me, that upon a catechising day, when Sir Roger has been pleased with a boy that answers well, he has ordered a bible to be given him next day for his encouragement; and sometimes accompanies it with a flitch of bacon to his mother. Sir Roger has likewise added five pounds a year to the clerk's place; and that he may encourage the young fellows to make themselves perfect in the church-service, has promised, upon the death of the present incumbent, who is very old, to bestow it according to merit.

The fair understanding between Sir Roger and his chaplain, and their mutual concurrence in doing good, is the more remarkable, because the very next village is famous for the differences and contentions that rise between the parson and the 'squire, who live in a perpetual state of war. The parson is always preaching at the 'squire, and the 'squire to be revenged on the parson never comes to church. The 'squire has made all his tenants atheists, and tithe-stealers; while the parson instructs them every Sunday in the dignity of his order, and insinuates to them in almost every sermon that he is a better man than his patron. In short matters have come to such an extremity, that the 'squire has not said his prayers either in public or private this half year; and that the parson threatens him, if he does not mend his manners, to pray for him in the face of the whole congregation.

Feuds of this nature, though too frequent in the country, are very fatal to the ordinary people; who are so used to be dazzled with riches, that they pay as much deference to the understanding of a man of an estate, as of a man of learning: and are very hardly brought to regard any truth, how important soever it may be, that is preached to them, when they know there are several men of five hundred a year who do not believe it. L.

SIR ROGER IN LOVE. [STEELE.]

NO. 113. — TUESDAY, JULY 10, 1711.

HÆRENT infixi pectore vultus. — VIRG. ÆN. iv. 4.

HER looks were deep imprinted in his heart.

IN my first description of the company in which I pass most of my time, it may be remembered, that I mentioned a great affliction which my friend Sir Roger had met with in his youth; which was no less than a disappointment in love. It happened this evening, that we fell into a very pleasing walk at a distance from his house. As soon as we came into it, "It is," quoth the good old man, looking round him with a smile, "very hard, that any part of my land should be settled upon one who has used me so ill as the perverse widow did; and yet I am sure I could not see a sprig of any bough of this whole walk of trees, but I should reflect upon her and her severity. She has certainly the finest hand of any woman in the world. You are to know, this was the place wherein I used to muse upon her; and by that custom I can never come into it, but the same tender sentiments revive in my mind, as if I had actually walked with that beautiful creature under these shades. I have been fool enough to carve her name on the bark of several of these trees; so unhappy is the condition of men in love, to attempt the removing of their passion by the methods which serve only to imprint it deeper. She has certainly the finest hand of any woman in the world."

Here followed a profound silence; and I was not displeased to observe my friend falling so naturally into a discourse which I had ever before taken notice he industriously avoided. After a very long pause, he entered upon an account of this great circumstance in his life, with an air which I thought raised my idea of him above what I had ever had before; and gave me the picture of that cheerful mind of his, before it received that stroke which has ever since affected his words and actions. But he went on as follows: —

"I came to my estate in my twenty-second year, and resolved to follow the steps of the most worthy of my ancestors who have inhabited this spot of earth before me, in all the methods of hospitality and good neighbourhood, for the sake of my fame; and in country sports and recreations, for the sake of my health. In my twenty-third year I was obliged to serve as sheriff of the county; and in my servants, officers, and whole equipage, indulged the pleasure of a young man (who did not think ill of his own person) in taking that public occasion of showing my figure and behaviour to advantage. You may easily imagine to yourself what appearance I made, who am pretty tall, ride well, and was very well dressed, at the head of a whole county, with music before me, a feather in my hat, and my horse well bitted. I can assure you I was not a little pleased with the kind looks and glances I had from all the balconies and windows as I rode to the hall where the assizes were held. But, when I came there, a beautiful creature in a widow's habit sat in a court to hear the event of a cause concerning her dower. This commanding creature (who was born for the destruction of all who behold her) put on such a resignation in her countenance, and bore the whispers of all around the court with such a pretty uneasiness, I warrant you, and then recovered herself from one eye to another, until she was perfectly confused by meeting something so wistful in all she encountered, that at last, with a murrain to her, she cast her bewitching eye upon me. I no sooner met it but I bowed like a great surprised booby; and knowing her cause to be the first which came on, I cried, like a captivated calf as I was, 'Make way for the defendant's witnesses.' This sudden partiality made all the county immediately see the sheriff also was become a slave to the fine widow. During the time her cause was upon trial, she behaved herself, I warrant you, with such a deep attention to her business, took opportunities to have little billets handed to her counsel, then would be in such a pretty confusion, occasioned, you must know, by acting before so much company, that not only I but the whole court was prejudiced in her favour; and all that the next heir to her husband had to urge was thought so groundless and frivolous, that when it came to her counsel to reply, there was not half so much said as every one besides in the court thought he could have urged to her advantage. You must understand, Sir, this perverse woman is one of those unaccountable creatures that secretly rejoice in the admiration of men, but indulge themselves in no farther consequences. Hence it is that she has ever had a train of admirers, and she removes from her slaves in town to those in the country, according to the seasons of the year. She is a reading lady, and far gone in the pleasures of friendship. She is always accompanied by a confidante, who is witness to her daily protestations against our sex, and consequently a bar to her first steps towards love, upon the strength of her own maxims and declarations.

"However, I must needs say, this accomplished mistress of mine has distinguished me above the rest, and has been known to declare Sir Roger de Coverley was the tamest and most humane of all the brutes in the country. I was told she said so by one who thought he rallied me; and upon the strength of this slender encouragement of being thought least detestable, I made new liveries, new-paired my coach-horses, sent them all to town to be bitted, and taught to throw their legs well, and move all together, before I pretended to cross the country, and wait upon her. As soon as I thought my retinue suitable to the character of my fortune and youth, I set out from hence to make my addresses. The particular skill of this lady has ever been to inflame your wishes, and yet command respect. To make her mistress of this art, she has a greater share of knowledge, wit, and good sense than is usual even among men of merit. Then she is beautiful beyond the race of women. If you will not let her go on with a certain artifice with her eyes, and the skill of beauty, she will arm herself with her real charms, and strike you with admiration instead of desire. It is certain that if you were to behold the whole woman, there is that dignity in her aspect, that composure in her motion, that complacency in her manner, that if her form makes you hope, her merit makes you fear. But then again, she is such a desperate scholar that no country gentleman can approach her without being a jest. As I was going to tell you, when I came to her house, I was admitted to her presence with great civility; at the same time she placed herself to be first seen by me in such an attitude, as I think you call the posture of a picture, that she discovered new charms, and I at last came towards her with such an awe as made me speechless. This she no sooner observed but she made her advantage of it, and began a discourse to me concerning love and honour, as they both are followed by pretenders, and the real votaries to them. When she discussed these points in a discourse which, I verily believe, was as learned as the best philosopher in Europe could possibly make, she asked me whether she was so happy as to fall in with my sentiments on these important particulars. Her confidante sat by her, and on my being in the last confusion and silence, this malicious aid of hers turning to her, says, 'I am very glad to observe Sir Roger pauses upon this subject, and seems resolved to deliver all his sentiments upon the matter when he pleases to speak.' They both kept their countenances, and after I had sat half an hour meditating how to behave before such profound casuists, I rose up and took my leave. Chance has since that time thrown me very often in her way, and she as often directed a discourse to me which I do not understand. This barbarity has kept me ever at a distance from the most beautiful object my eyes ever beheld. It is thus also she deals with all mankind, and you must make love to her as you would conquer the sphinx, by posing her. But were she like other women, and that there were any talking to her, how constant must the pleasure of that man be, who could converse with a creature — But, after all, you may be sure her heart is fixed on some one or other: and yet I have been credibly informed — but who can believe half that is said! — They say she sings excellently: her voice in her ordinary speech has something in it inexpressibly sweet. You must know I dined with her at a public table the day after I first saw her, and she helped me to some tansy in the eye of all the gentlemen in the country. She has certainly the finest hand of any woman in the world. I can assure you, Sir, were you to behold her, you would be in the same condition; for as her speech is music, her form is angelic. But I find I grow irregular while I am talking of her; but indeed it would be stupidity to be unconcerned at such perfection. Oh, the excellent creature! she is as inimitable to all women, as she is inaccessible to all men."

I found my friend begin to rave, and insensibly led him towards the house, that we might be joined by some other company; and am convinced that the widow is the secret cause of all that inconsistency which appears in some parts of my friend's discourse; though he has so much command of himself as not directly to mention her, yet according to that of Martial, which one knows not how to render into English, *dum tacet hanc loquitur*. I shall end this paper with that whole epigram, which represents with much humour my honest friend's condition: —

Quicquid agit Rufus, nihil est, nisi Nævia Rufo,
  Si gaudet, si flet, si tacet, hanc loquitur:
Cœnat, propinat, poscit, negat, annuit, una est
  Nævia: si non sit Nævia, mutus erit.
Scriberit hesterna patri cum luce salutem,
  Nævia lux, inquit, Nævia numen, ave.

Let Rufus weep, rejoice, stand, sit, or walk,
Still he can nothing but of Nævia talk;
Let him eat, drink, ask questions, or dispute,
Still he must speak of Nævia, or be mute.
He writ to his father, ending with this line,
I am, my lovely Nævia, ever thine.

R.

SIR ROGER'S ECONOMY. [STEELE.]

No 114.—WEDNESDAY, JULY 11, 1711.

PAUPERTATIS pudor et fuga.

— HOR. LIB. 1 EP. xviii. 24.

THE dread of nothing more
Than to be thought necessitous and poor. — POOLY.

ECONOMY in our affairs has the same effect upon our fortunes which good-breeding has upon our conversation. There is a pretending behaviour in both cases, which, instead of making men esteemed, renders them both miserable and contemptible. We had yesterday, at Sir Roger's, a set of country gentlemen who dined with him: and after dinner the glass was taken, by those who pleased, pretty plentifully. Among others I observed a person of a tolerable good aspect, who seemed to be more greedy of liquor than any of the company, and yet methought he did not taste it with delight. As he grew warm, he was suspicious of every thing that was said, and as he advanced towards being fuddled, his humour grew worse. At the same time his bitterness seemed to be rather an inward dissatisfaction in his own mind, than any dislike he had taken to the company. Upon hearing his name, I knew him to be a gentleman of a considerable fortune in this county, but greatly in debt. What gives the unhappy man this peevishness of spirit is, that his estate is dipped, and is eating out with usury; and yet he has not the heart to sell any part of it. His proud stomach, at the cost of restless nights, constant inquietudes, danger of affronts, and a thousand nameless inconveniences, preserves this canker in his fortune, rather than it shall be said he is a man of fewer hundreds a year than he has been commonly reputed. Thus he endures the torment of poverty to avoid the name of being less rich. If you go to his house, you see great plenty; but served in a manner that shews it is all unnatural, and that the master's mind is not at home. There is a certain waste and carelessness in the air of every thing, and the whole appears but a covered indigence, a magnificent poverty. That neatness and cheerfulness which attend the table of him who lives within compass, is wanting, and exchanged for a libertine way of service in all about him.

This gentleman's conduct, though a very common way of management, is as ridiculous as that officer's would be, who had but few men under his command, and should take the charge of an extent of country rather than of a small pass. To pay for, personate, and keep in a man's hands, a greater estate than he really has, is of all others the most unpardonable vanity, and must in the end reduce the man who is guilty of it to dishonour. Yet if we look round us in any county of Great Britain, we shall see many in this fatal error; if that may be called by so soft a name, which proceeds from a false shame of appearing what they really are, when the contrary behaviour would in a short time advance them to the condition which they pretend to.

Laertes has fifteen hundred pounds a year; which is mortgaged for six thousand pounds; but it is impossible to convince him, that if he sold as much as would pay off that debt, he would save four shillings in the pound, which he gives for the vanity of being the reputed master of it. Yet if Laertes did this, he would perhaps be easier in his own fortunes; but then Irus, a fellow of yesterday, who has but twelve hundred a year, would be his equal. Rather than this should be, Laertes goes on to bring well-born beggars into the world, and every twelvemonth charges his estate with at least one year's rent more by the birth of a child.

Laertes and Irus are neighbours, whose way of living are an abomination to each other. Irus is moved by the fear of poverty, and Laertes by the shame of it. Though the motive of action is of so near affinity in both, and may be resolved into this, 'that to each of them poverty is the greatest of all evils,' yet are their manners very widely different. Shame of poverty makes Laertes launch into unnecessary equipage, vain expense, and lavish entertainments. Fear of poverty makes Irus allow himself only plain necessaries, appear without a servant, sell his own corn, attend his labourers, and be himself a labourer. Shame of poverty makes Laertes go every day a step nearer to it; and fear of poverty stirs up Irus to make every day some farther progress from it.

These different motives produce the excesses which men are guilty of in the negligence of and provision for themselves. Usury, stock-jobbing, extortion, and oppression, have their seed in the dread of want; and vanity, riot, and prodigality, from the shame of it: but both these excesses are infinitely below the pursuit of a reasonable creature. After we have taken care to command so much as is necessary for maintaining ourselves in the order of men suitable to our character, the care of superfluities is a vice no less extravagant than the neglect of necessaries would have been before.

Certain it is, that they are both out of nature, when she is followed with reason and good sense. It is from this reflection that I always read Mr. Cowley with the greatest pleasure. His magnanimity is as much above that of other considerable men, as his understanding; and it is a true distinguishing spirit in the elegant author who published his works, to dwell so much upon the temper of his mind and the moderation of his desires. By this means he rendered his friend as amiable as famous. That state of life which bears the face of poverty with Mr. Cowley's great vulgar, is admirably described; and it is no small satisfaction to those of the same turn of desire, that he produces the authority of the wisest men of the best age of the world, to strengthen his opinion of the ordinary pursuits of mankind.

It would methinks be no ill maxim of life, if, according to that ancestor of Sir Roger, whom I lately mentioned, every man would point to himself what sum he would resolve not to exceed. He might by this means cheat himself into a tranquillity on this side of that expectation, or convert what he should get above it to nobler uses than his own pleasures or necessities. This temper of mind would exempt a man from an ignorant envy of restless men above him, and a more inexcusable contempt of happy men below him. This would be sailing by some compass, living with some design; but to be eternally bewildered in prospects of future gain, and putting on unnecessary armour against improbable blows of fortune, is a mechanic being which has not good sense for its direction, but is carried on by a sort of acquired instinct towards things below our consideration, and unworthy our esteem. It is possible that the tranquillity I now enjoy at Sir Roger's may have created in me this way of thinking, which is so abstracted from the common relish of the world; but as I am now in a pleasant arbour surrounded with a beautiful landscape, I find no inclination so strong as to continue in these mansions so remote from the ostentatious scenes of life; and am at this present writing philosopher enough to conclude with Mr. Cowley,

'If e'er ambition did my fancy cheat
With any wish so mean as to be great;
Continue, Heav'n, still from me to remove
The humble blessings of that life I love.'

T.

THE SPECTATOR ON EXERCISE. [ADDISON.]

No. 115. — THURSDAY, JULY 12, 1711.

UT sit mens sana in corpore sano. — JUV. SAT. x. 356.

A HEALTHY body and a mind at ease.

BODILY labour is of two kinds, either that which a man submits to for his livelihood, or that which he undergoes for his pleasure. The latter of them generally changes the name of labour for that of exercise, but differs only from ordinary labour as it rises from another motive.

A country life abounds in both these kinds of labour, and for that reason gives a man a greater stock of health, and consequently a more perfect enjoyment of himself, than any other way of life. I consider the body as a system of tubes and glands, or, to use a more rustic phrase, a bundle of pipes and strainers, fitted to one another after so wonderful a manner as to make a proper engine for the soul to work with. This description does not only comprehend the bowels, bones, tendons, veins, nerves, and arteries, but every muscle and every ligature, which is a composition of fibres, that are so many imperceptible tubes or pipes interwoven on all sides with invisible glands or strainers.

This general idea of a human body, without considering it in its niceties of anatomy, lets us see how absolutely necessary labour is for the right preservation of it. There must be frequent motions and agitations, to mix, digest, and separate the juices contained in it, as well as to clear and cleanse that infinitude of pipes and strainers of which it is composed, and to give their solid parts a more firm and lasting tone. Labour or exercise ferments the humours, casts them into their proper channels, throws off redundancies, and helps nature in those secret distributions, without which the body cannot subsist in its vigour, nor the soul act with cheerfulness.

I might here mention the effects which this has upon all the faculties of the mind, by keeping the understanding clear, the imagination untroubled, and refining those spirits that are necessary for the proper exertion of our intellectual faculties, during the present laws of union between soul and body. It is to a neglect in this particular that we must ascribe the spleen, which is so frequent in men of studious and sedentary tempers, as well as the vapours, to which those of the other sex are so often subject.

Had not exercise been absolutely necessary for our well-being, nature would not have made the body so proper for it, by giving such an activity to the limbs, and such a pliancy to every part, as necessarily produce those compressions, extensions, contortions, dilatations, and all other kinds of motions that are necessary for the preservation of such a system of tubes and glands as has been before mentioned. And that we might not want inducements to engage us in such an exercise of the body as is proper for its welfare, it is so ordered, that nothing valuable can be procured without it. Not to mention riches and honour, even food and raiment are not to be come at without the toil of the hands and sweat of the brows. Providence furnishes materials, but expects that we should work them up ourselves. The earth must be laboured before it gives its increase, and when it is forced into its several products, how many hands must they pass through before they are fit for use? Manufactures, trade and agriculture, naturally employ more than nineteen parts of the species in twenty; and as for those who are not obliged to labour, by the condition in which they are born, they are more miserable than the rest of mankind, unless they indulge themselves in that voluntary labour which goes by the name of exercise.

My friend Sir Roger has been an indefatigable man in business of this kind, and has hung several parts of his house with the trophies of his former labours. The walls of his great hall are covered with the horns of several kinds of deer that he has killed in the chase, which he thinks the most valuable furniture of his house, as they afford him frequent topics of discourse, and shew that he has not been idle. At the lower end of the hall, is a large otter's skin stuffed with hay, which his mother ordered to be hung up in that manner, and the knight looks upon it with great satisfaction, because it seems he was but nine years old when his dog killed him. A little room adjoining to the hall is a kind of arsenal filled with guns of several sizes and inventions, with which the knight has made great havoc in the woods, and destroyed many thousands of pheasants, partridges, and woodcocks. His stable doors are patched with noses that belonged to foxes of the knight's own hunting down. Sir Roger shewed me one of them that for distinction's sake has a brass nail struck through it, which cost him about fifteen hours' riding, carried him through half a dozen counties, killed him a brace of geldings, and lost above half his dogs. This the knight looks upon as one of the greatest exploits of his life. The perverse widow, whom I have given some account of, was the death of several foxes; for Sir Roger has told me, that in the course of his amours he patched the western door of his stable. Whenever the widow was cruel, the foxes were sure to pay for it. In proportion as his passion for the widow abated, and old age came on, he left off fox-hunting; but a hare is not yet safe that sits within ten miles of his house.

There is no kind of exercise which I would so recommend to my readers of both sexes as this of riding, as there is none which so much conduces to health, and is every way accommodated to the body, according to the idea which I have given of it. Dr. Sydenham is very lavish in its praises; and if the English reader will see the mechanical effects of it described at length, he may find them in a book published not many years since, under the title of *Medicina Gymnastica*. For my own part, when I am in town, for want of these opportunities, I exercise myself an hour every morning upon a dumb bell that is placed in a corner of my room, and pleases me the more, because it does every thing I require of it in the most profound silence. My landlady and her daughters are so well acquainted with my hours of exercise, that they never come into my room to disturb me whilst I am ringing.

When I was some years younger than I am at present, I used to employ myself in a more laborious diversion, which I learned from a Latin treatise of exercises that is written with great erudition: it is there called the *σκιομαχία*, or the fighting with a man's own shadow, and consists in the brandishing of two short sticks grasped in each hand, and loaden with plugs of lead at either end. This opens the chest, exercises the limbs, and gives a man all the pleasure of boxing without the blows. I could wish that several learned men would lay out that time which they employ in controversies and disputes about nothing, in this method of fighting with their own shadows. It might conduce very much to evaporate the spleen, which makes them uneasy to the public as well as to themselves.

To conclude, as I am a compound of soul and body, I consider myself as obliged to a double scheme of duties; and think I have not fulfilled the business of the day, when I do not thus employ the one in labour and exercise, as well as the other in study and contemplation. L.

SIR ROGER AS A HUNTER. [BUDGELL.]

NO. 116. — FRIDAY, JULY 13, 1711.

VOCAT ingenti clamore Cithæron,
Taygetique canes. — VIRG. GEORG. iii. 43.

THE echoing hills and chiding hounds invite.

THOSE who have searched into human nature observe, that nothing so much shews the nobleness of the soul, as that its felicity consists in action. Every man has such an active principle in him, that he will find out something to employ himself upon, in whatever place or state of life he is posted. I have heard of a gentleman who was under close confinement in the Bastile seven years; during which time he amused himself in scattering a few small pins about his chamber, gathering them up again, and placing them in different figures on the arm of a great chair. He often told his friends afterwards, that unless he had found out this piece of exercise, he verily believed he should have lost his senses.

After what has been said, I need not inform my readers, that Sir Roger, with whose character I hope they are at present pretty well acquainted, has in his youth gone through the whole course of those rural diversions which the country abounds in; and which seem to be extremely well suited to that laborious industry a man may observe here in a far greater degree than in towns and cities. I have before hinted at some of my friend's exploits; he has in his youthful days taken forty coveys of partridges in a season; and tired many a salmon with a line consisting but of a single hair. The constant thanks and good wishes of the neighbourhood always attended him, on account of his remarkable enmity towards foxes; having destroyed more of those vermin in one year, than it was thought the whole county could have produced. Indeed the knight does not scruple to own among his most intimate friends, that in order to establish his reputation this way, he has secretly sent for great numbers of them out of other counties, which he used to turn loose about the country by night, that he might the better signalise himself in their destruction the next day. His hunting horses were the finest and best managed in all these parts. His tenants are still full of the praises of a grey stone horse that unhappily staked himself several years since, and was buried with great solemnity in the orchard.

Sir Roger, being at present too old for fox-hunting, to keep himself in action, has disposed of his beagles and got a pack of stop-hounds. What these want in speed, he endeavours to make amends for by the deepness of their mouths and the variety of their notes, which are suited in such a manner to each other, that the whole cry makes up a complete concert. He is so nice in this particular, that a gentleman having made him a present of a very fine hound the other day, the knight returned it by the servant with a great many expressions of civility; but desired him to tell his master, that the dog he had sent was indeed a most excellent bass, but that at present he only wanted a counter-tenor. Could I believe my friend had ever read Shakspeare, I should certainly conclude he had taken the hint from Theseus in the Midsummer Night's Dream :

> "My hounds are bred out of the Spartan kind,
> So flu'd, so sanded; and their heads are hung
> With ears that sweep away the morning dew.
> Crook-knee'd and dew-lapp'd like Thessalian bulls,
> Slow in pursuit, but match'd in mouths like bells,
> Each under each. A cry more tunable
> Was never halloo'd to, nor cheer'd with horn."
>
> ACT iv. sc. 1.

Sir Roger is so keen at this sport that he has been out almost every day since I came down; and upon the chaplain's offering to lend me his easy pad, I was prevailed on yesterday morning to make one of the company. I was extremely pleased, as we rid along, to observe the general benevolence of all the neighbourhood towards my friend. The farmers' sons thought themselves happy if they could open a gate for the good old knight as he passed by; which he generally requited with a nod or a smile, and a kind inquiry after their fathers and uncles.

After we had rid about a mile from home, we came upon a large heath, and the sportsmen began to beat. They had done so for some time, when, as I was at a little distance from the rest of the company, I saw a hare pop out from a small furze-brake almost under my horse's feet. I marked the way she took, which I endeavoured to make the company sensible of by extending my arm; but to no purpose, till Sir Roger, who knows that none of my extraordinary motions are insignificant, rode up to me and asked me if puss was gone that way? Upon my answering "Yes," he immediately called in the dogs, and put them upon the scent. As they were going off, I heard one of the country-fellows muttering to his companion, that 'twas a wonder they had not lost all their sport, for want of the silent gentleman's crying, "Stole away."

This, with my aversion to leaping hedges, made me withdraw to a rising ground, from whence I could have the pleasure of the whole chase, without the fatigue of keeping in with the hounds. The hare immediately threw them above a mile behind her; but I was pleased to find, that instead of running straight forwards, or, in hunter's language, "flying the country," as I was afraid she might have done, she wheeled about, and described a sort of circle round the hill, where I had taken my station, in such manner as gave me a very distinct view of the sport. I could see her first pass by, and the dogs some time afterwards, unravelling the whole track she had made, and following her through all her doubles. I was at the same time delighted in observing that deference which the rest of the pack paid to each particular hound, according to the character he had acquired among them: if they were at a fault, and an old hound of reputation opened but once, he was immediately followed by the whole cry; while a raw dog, or one who was a noted liar, might have yelped his heart out without being taken notice of.

The hare now, after having squatted two or three

times, and been put up again as often, came still nearer to the place where she was at first started. The dogs pursued her, and these were followed by the jolly knight, who rode upon a white gelding, encompassed by his tenants and servants, and cheering his hounds with all the gayety of five and twenty. One of the sportsmen rode up to me, and told me that he was sure the chase was almost at an end, because the old dogs, which had hitherto lain behind, now headed the pack. The fellow was in the right. Our hare took a large field just under us, followed by the full cry in view. I must confess the brightness of the weather, the cheerfulness of every thing around me, the chiding of the hounds, which was returned upon us in a double echo from two neighbouring hills, with the hallooing of the sportsmen, and the sounding of the horn, lifted my spirits into a most lively pleasure, which I freely indulged because I was sure it was innocent. If I was under any concern, it was on account of the poor hare, that was now quite spent, and almost within the reach of her enemies; when the huntsman getting forward, threw down his pole before the dogs. They were now within eight yards of that game which they had been pursuing for almost as many hours; yet on the signal before mentioned they all made a sudden stand, and though they continued opening as much as before, durst not once attempt to pass beyond the pole. At the same time Sir Roger rode forward, and alighting, took up the hare in his arms; which he soon after delivered up to one of his servants with an order, if she could be kept alive, to let her go in his great orchard; where it seems he has several of these prisoners of war, who live together in a very comfortable captivity. I was highly pleased to see the discipline of the pack, and the good-nature of the knight, who could not find in his heart to murder a creature that had given him so much diversion.

As we were returning home, I remembered that Monsieur Paschal, in his most excellent discourse on the misery of man, tells us, that all our endeavours after greatness proceed from nothing but a desire of being surrounded by a multitude of persons and affairs that may hinder us from looking into ourselves, which is a view we cannot bear. He afterwards goes on to show that our love of sports comes from the same reason, and is particularly severe upon hunting. "What," says he, "unless it be to drown thought, can make men throw away so much time and pains upon a silly animal, which they might buy cheaper in the market?" The foregoing reflexion is certainly just, when a man suffers his whole mind to be drawn into his sports, and altogether loses himself in the woods; but does not affect those who propose a far more laudable end from this exercise, I mean the preservation of health, and keeping all the organs of the soul in a condition to execute her orders. Had that incomparable person, whom I last quoted, been a little more indulgent to himself in this point, the world might probably have enjoyed him much longer; whereas through too great an application to his studies in his youth, he contracted that ill habit of body, which, after a tedious sickness, carried him off in the fortieth year of his age; and the whole history we have of his life till that time, is but one continued account of the behaviour of a noble soul struggling under innumerable pains and distempers.

For my own part, I intend to hunt twice a week during my stay with Sir Roger; and shall prescribe the moderate use of this exercise to all my country friends, as the best kind of physic for mending a bad constitution, and preserving a good one.

I cannot do this better, than in the following lines out of Mr. Dryden:

> "The first physicians by debauch were made;
> Excess began, and Sloth sustains the trade.
> By chase our long-liv'd fathers earn'd their food;
> Toil strung the nerves, and purified the blood;
> But we their sons, a pamper'd race of men,
> Are dwindled down to threescore years and ten.
> Better to hunt in fields for health unbought,
> Than fee the doctor for a nauseous draught.
> The wise for cure on exercise depend:
> God never made his work for man to mend."

X.

A Cockfight

The fastidious gentleman hanging over the rail is a disgusted Frenchman. The blind man in the center is Lord Albemarle Bertie, who, though blind, so loved a cockfight that he followed the sport by the cries of the spectators.

AN INN COURT YARD

From a billhead designed by Hogarth. (*Boston Public Library.*)

MOLL WHITE. [ADDISON.]

NO. 117.—SATURDAY, JULY 14, 1711.

IPSI sibi somnia fingunt.—VIRG. ECL. viii. 108.

WITH voluntary dreams they cheat their minds.

THERE are some opinions in which a man should stand neuter without engaging his assent to one side or the other. Such a hovering faith as this, which refuses to settle upon any determination, is absolutely necessary in a mind that is careful to avoid errors and prepossessions. When the arguments press equally on both sides in matters that are indifferent to us, the safest method is to give up ourselves to neither.

It is with this temper of mind that I consider the subject of witchcraft. When I hear the relations that are made from all parts of the world, not only from Norway and Lapland, from the East and West Indies, but from every particular nation in Europe, I cannot forbear thinking that there is such an intercourse and commerce with evil spirits, as that which we express by the name of witchcraft. But when I consider that the ignorant and credulous parts of the world abound the most in these relations, and that the persons among us who are supposed to engage in such an infernal commerce are people of a weak understanding and crazed imagination, and at the same time reflect upon the many impostures and delusions of this nature that have been detected in all ages, I endeavour to suspend my belief till I hear more certain accounts than any which have yet come to my knowledge. In short, when I consider the question, whether there are such persons in the world, as those we call witches, my mind is divided between the two opposite opinions; or rather (to speak my thoughts freely) I believe in general that there is and has been such a thing as witchcraft; but at the same time can give no credit to any particular instance of it.

I am engaged in this speculation, by some occurrences that I met with yesterday, which I shall give my reader an account of at large. As I was walking with my friend Sir Roger by the side of one of his woods, an old woman applied herself to me for my charity. Her dress and figure put me in mind of the following description in *Otway*.

"In a close lane as I pursued my journey,
I espied a wrinkled hag, with age grown double,
Picking dry sticks, and mumbling to herself.
Her eyes with scalding rheum were gall'd and red;
Cold palsy shook her head; her hands seem'd wither'd;
And on her crooked shoulders had she wrapp'd
The tatter'd remnants of an old stripp'd hanging;
Which serv'd to keep her carcase from the cold:
So there was nothing of a piece about her.
Her lower weeds were all o'er coarsely patch'd
With diff'rent colour'd rags, black, red, white, yellow,
And seem'd to speak variety of wretchedness."

As I was musing on this description, and comparing it with the object before me, the knight told me, that this very old woman had the reputation of a witch all over the country, that her lips were observed to be always in motion, and that there was not a switch about her house which her neighbours did not believe had carried her several hundreds of miles. If she chanced to stumble, they always found sticks or straws that lay in the figure of a cross before her. If she made any mistake at church, and cried *Amen* in a wrong place, they never failed to conclude that she was saying her prayers backwards. There was not a maid in the parish that would take a pin of her, though she should offer a bag of money with it. She goes by the name of Moll White, and has made the country ring with several imaginary exploits that are palmed upon her. If the dairy-maid does not make her butter come so soon as she would have it, Moll White is at the bottom of the churn. If a horse sweats in the stable, Moll White has been upon his back. If a hare makes an unexpected escape from the hounds, the huntsman curses Moll White. Nay (says Sir Roger) I have known the master of the pack, upon such an occasion, send one of his servants to see if Moll White had been out that morning.

This account raised my curiosity so far, that I begged my friend Sir Roger to go with me into her hovel, which stood in a solitary corner under the side of the wood. Upon our first entering Sir Roger winked to me, and pointed at something that stood behind the door, which, upon looking that way, I found to be an old broomstaff. At the same time he whispered me in the ear to take notice of a tabby cat that sat in the chimney corner, which, as the old knight told me, lay under as bad a report as Moll White herself; for besides that Moll is said often to accompany her in the same shape, the cat is reported to have spoken twice or thrice in her life, and to have played several pranks above the capacity of an ordinary cat.

I was secretly concerned to see human nature in so much wretchedness and disgrace, but at the same time could not forbear smiling to hear Sir Roger, who is a little puzzled about the old woman, advising her, as a justice of the peace, to avoid all communication with the devil, and never to hurt any of her neighbours' cattle. We concluded our visit with a bounty, which was very acceptable.

In our return home, Sir Roger told me that old Moll had been often brought before him for making children spit pins, and giving maids the night mare; and that the country people would be tossing her into a pond, and trying experiments with her every day, if it was not for him and his chaplain.

I have since found upon inquiry, that Sir Roger was several times staggered with the reports that had been brought him concerning this old woman, and would frequently have bound her over to the county sessions, had not his chaplain with much ado persuaded him to the contrary.

I have been the more particular in this account, because I hear there is scarce a village in England that has not a Moll White in it. When an old woman begins to dote and grow chargeable to a parish, she is generally turned into a witch, and fills the whole country with extravagant fancies, imaginary distempers, and terrifying dreams. In the mean time, the poor wretch that is the innocent occasion of so many evils begins to be frighted at herself, and sometimes confesses secret commerces and familiarities that her imagination forms in a delirious old age. This frequently cuts off charity from the greatest objects of compassion, and inspires people with a malevolence towards those poor decrepit parts of our species, in whom human nature is defaced by infirmity and dotage. **L.**

A COVERLEY PASTORAL. [STEELE.]

No. 118.—MONDAY, JULY 16, 1711.

HÆRET lateri lethalis rundo.—VIRG. ÆN. iv. 73.

THE fatal dart
Sticks in his side, and rankles in his heart.—DRYDEN.

THIS agreeable seat is surrounded with so many pleasing walks, which are struck out of a wood, in the midst of which the house stands, that one can hardly ever be weary of rambling from one labyrinth of delight to another. To one used to live in a city, the charms of the country are so exquisite that the mind is lost in a certain transport which raises us above ordinary life, and is yet not strong enough to be inconsistent with tranquillity. This state of mind was I in—ravished with the murmur of waters, the whisper of breezes, the singing of birds; and whether I looked up to the heavens, down on the earth, or turned to the prospects around me, still struck with new sense of pleasure;—when I found by the voice of my friend, who walked by me, that we had insensibly strolled into the grove sacred to the widow. "This woman," says he, "is of all others the most unintelligible: she either designs to marry, or she does not. What is the most perplexing of all is, that she does not either say to her lovers she has any resolution against that condition of life in general, or that she banishes them; but, conscious of her own merit, she permits their addresses, without fear of any ill consequence, or want of respect, from their rage or despair. She has that in her aspect against which it is impossible to offend. A man whose thoughts are constantly bent upon so agreeable an object, must be excused if the ordinary occurrences in conversation are below his attention. I call her indeed perverse, but, alas! why do I call her so? — because her superior merit is such, that I cannot approach her without awe — that my heart is checked by too much esteem: I am angry that her charms are not more accessible — that I am more inclined to worship than salute her. How often have I wished her unhappy, that I might have an opportunity of serving her! and how often troubled in that very imagination at giving her the pain of being obliged! Well, I have led a miserable life in secret upon her account; but fancy she would have condescended to have some regard for me, if it had not been for that watchful animal her confidante.

"Of all persons under the sun" (continued he, calling me by name) "be sure to set a mark upon confidantes: they are of all people the most impertinent. What is most pleasant to observe in them is, that they assume to themselves the merit of the persons whom they have in their custody. Orestilla is a great fortune, and in wonderful danger of surprises, therefore full of suspicions of the least indifferent thing, particularly careful of new acquaintance, and of growing too familiar with the old. Themista, her favourite woman, is every whit as careful of whom she speaks to, and what she says. Let the ward be a beauty, her confidante shall treat you with an air of distance; let her be a fortune, and she assumes the suspicious behaviour of her friend and patroness. Thus it is that very many of our unmarried women of distinction are to all intents and purposes married, except the consideration of different sexes. They are directly under the conduct of their whisperer; and think they are in a state of freedom, while they can prate with one of these attendants of all men in general, and still avoid the man they most like. You do not see one heiress in a hundred whose fate does not turn upon this circumstance of choosing a confidante. Thus it is that the lady is addressed to, presented and flattered, only by proxy, in her woman. In my case, how is it possible that ——," Sir Roger was proceeding in his harangue, when we heard the voice of one speaking very importunately, and repeating these words, "What, not one smile?" We followed the sound till we came to a close thicket, on the other side of which we saw a young woman sitting as it were in a personated sullenness just over a transparent fountain. Opposite to her stood Mr. William, Sir Roger's master of the game. The knight whispered me, "Hist, these are lovers." The huntsman looking earnestly at the shadow of the young maiden in the stream — "Oh, thou dear picture, if thou couldst remain there in the absence of that fair creature whom you represent in the water, how willingly could I stand here satisfied for ever, without troubling my dear Betty herself with any mention of her unfortunate William whom she is angry with! But alas! when she pleases to be gone, thou wilt also vanish — yet let me talk to thee while thou dost stay. Tell my dearest Betty thou dost not more depend upon her than does her William; her absence will make away with me as well as thee. If she offers to remove thee, I will jump into these waves to lay hold on thee — herself, her own dear person, I must never embrace again. Still do you hear me without one smile — it is too much to bear." He had no sooner spoke these words, but he made an offer of throwing himself into the water: at which his mistress started up, and at the next instant he jumped across the fountain, and met her in an embrace. She, half recovering from her fright, said in the most charming voice imaginable, and with a tone of complaint, "I thought how well you would drown yourself. No, no, you will not drown yourself till you have taken your leave of Susan Holiday." The huntsman, with a tenderness that spoke the most passionate love, and with his cheek close to hers, whispered the softest vows of fidelity in her ear, and cried, "Do not, my dear, believe a word Kate Willow says; she is spiteful, and makes stories, because she loves to hear me talk to herself for your sake." "Look you there," quoth Sir Roger, "do you see there, all mischief comes from confidantes! But let us not interrupt them; the maid is honest, and the man dares not be otherwise, for he knows I loved her father: I will interpose in this matter, and hasten the wedding. Kate Willow is a witty mischievous wench in the neighbourhood, who was a beauty; and makes me hope I shall see the perverse widow in her condition. She was so flippant in her answers to all the honest fellows that came near her, and so very vain of her beauty, that she has valued herself upon her charms till they are ceased. She therefore now makes it her business to prevent other young women from being more discreet than she was herself: however, the saucy thing said the other day well enough, 'Sir Roger and I must make a match, for we are both despised by those we loved.' The hussy has a great deal of power wherever she comes, and has her share of cunning.

"However, when I reflect upon this woman, I do not know whether in the main I am the worse for having loved her: whenever she is recalled to my imagination, my youth returns, and I feel a forgotten warmth in my veins. This affliction in my life has streaked all my conduct with a softness, of which I should otherwise have been incapable. It is owing, perhaps, to this dear image in my heart that I am apt to relent, that I easily forgive, and that many desirable things are grown into my temper, which I should not have arrived at by better motives than the thought of being one day hers. I am pretty well satisfied such a passion as I have had is never well cured; and between you and me, I am often apt to imagine it has had some whimsical effect upon my brain: for I frequently find, that in my most serious discourse I let fall some comical familiarity of speech or odd phrase that makes the company laugh. However, I cannot but allow she is a most excellent woman. When she is in the country, I warrant she does not run into dairies, but reads upon the nature of plants; she has a glass beehive, and comes into the garden out of books to see them work, and observe the policies of their commonwealth. She understands every thing. I would give ten pounds to hear her argue with my friend Sir Andrew Freeport about trade. No, no, for all she looks so innocent as it were, take my word for it she is no fool."

T.

COUNTRY MANNERS. [ADDISON.]

No. 119.—TUESDAY, JULY 17, 1711.

URBEM quam dicunt Romam, Melibœe, putavi
Stultus ego huic nostræ similem.—VIRG. ECL. i. 20.

THE city men call Rome, unskilful clown,
I thought resembled this our humble town.—WHARTON.

THE first and most obvious reflexions which arise in a man who changes the city for the country, are upon the different manners of the people whom he meets with in those two different scenes of life. By manners I do not mean morals, but behaviour and good breeding, as they shew themselves in the town and in the country.

And here, in the first place, I must observe a very great revolution that has happened in this article of good breeding. Several obliging deferences, condescensions, and submissions, with many outward forms and ceremonies that accompany them, were first of all brought up among the politer part of mankind, who lived in courts and cities, and distinguished themselves from the rustic part of the species (who on all occasions acted bluntly and naturally) by such a mutual complaisance and intercourse of civilities. These forms of conversation by degrees multiplied and grew troublesome; the modish world found too great a constraint in them, and have therefore thrown most of them aside. Conversation, like the Romish religion, was so encumbered with shew and ceremony, that it stood in need of a reformation to retrench its superfluities, and restore it to its natural good sense and beauty. At present, therefore, an unconstrained carriage and a certain openness of behaviour are the height of good breeding. The fashionable world is grown free and easy; our manners sit more loose upon us; nothing is so modish as an agreeable negligence. In a word, good breeding shews itself most where to an ordinary eye it appears the least.

If after this we look on the people of mode in the country, we find in them the manners of the last age. They have no sooner fetched themselves up to the fashion of the polite world, but the town has dropped them, and are nearer to the first state of nature than to those refinements which formerly reigned in the court, and still prevail in the country. One may now know a man that never conversed in the world, by his excess of good breeding. A polite country 'squire shall make you as many bows in half an hour as would serve a courtier for a week. There is infinitely more to do about place and precedency in a meeting of justices' wives than in an assembly of duchesses.

This rural politeness is very troublesome to a man of my temper, who generally take the chair that is next me, and walk first or last, in the front or in the rear, as chance directs. I have known my friend Sir Roger's dinner almost cold before the company could adjust the ceremonial, and be prevailed upon to sit down; and have heartily pitied my old friend, when I have seen him forced to pick and cull his guests, as they sat at the several parts of his table, that he might drink their healths according to their respective ranks and qualities. Honest Will Wimble, who I should have thought had been altogether uninfected with ceremony, gives me abundance of trouble in this particular. Though he has been fishing all the morning, he will not help himself at dinner until I am served. When we are going out of the hall, he runs behind me; and last night, as we were walking in the fields, stopped short at a stile until I came up to it, and upon my making signs to him to get over, told me, with a serious smile, that sure I believed they had no manners in the country.

There has happened another revolution in the point of good breeding, which relates to the conversation among men of mode, and which I cannot but look upon as very extraordinary. It was certainly one of the first distinctions of a well-bred man to express every thing that had the most remote appearance of being obscene in modest terms and distant phrases; whilst the clown, who had no such delicacy of conception and expression, clothed his ideas in those plain, homely terms that are the most obvious and natural. This kind of good manners was perhaps carried to an excess, so as to make conversation too stiff, formal, and precise; for which reason (as hypocrisy in one age is generally succeeded by atheism in another), conversation is in a great measure relapsed into the first extreme; so that at present several of our men of the town, and particularly those who have been polished in France, make use of the most coarse uncivilized words in our language, and utter themselves often in such a manner as a clown would blush to hear.

This infamous piece of good breeding, which reigns among the coxcombs of the town, has not yet made its way into the country; and as it is impossible for such an irrational way of conversation to last long among a people that make any profession of religion, or shew of modesty, if the country gentlemen get into it, they will certainly be left in the lurch. Their good breeding will come too late to them, and they will be thought a parcel of lewd clowns, while they fancy themselves talking together like men of wit and pleasure.

As the two points of good breeding which I have hitherto insisted upon regard behaviour and conversation, there is a third which turns upon dress. In this too the country are very much behindhand. The rural beaus are not yet got out of the fashion that took place at the time of the Revolution, but ride about the country in red coats and laced hats, while the women are still trying to outvie one another in the height of their head-dresses.

But a friend of mine, who is now upon the western circuit, having promised to give me an account of the several modes and fashions that prevail in the different parts of the nation through which he passes, I shall defer enlarging upon this last topic, till I have received a letter from him, which I expect every post. L.

THE SPECTATOR ON INSTINCT. [ADDISON.]

NO. 120. — WEDNESDAY, JULY 18, 1711.

EQUIDEM credo, quia sit divinitus illis
Ingenium. — VIRG. GEORG. i. 451.

I THINK their beasts with heav'nly souls inspired. — DRYDEN.

MY friend Sir Roger is very often merry with me upon my passing so much of my time among his poultry. He has caught me twice or thrice looking after a bird's-nest, and several times sitting an hour or two together near an hen and chickens. He tells me he believes I am personally acquainted with every fowl about his house; calls such a particular cock my favourite; and frequently complains that his ducks and geese have more of my company than himself.

I must confess I am infinitely delighted with those speculations of nature which are to be made in a country-life; and as my reading has very much lain among books of natural history, I cannot forbear recollecting upon this occasion the several remarks which I have met with in authors, and comparing them with what falls under my own observation: the arguments for providence drawn from the natural history of animals being in my opinion demonstrative.

The make of every kind of animal is different from that of every other kind: and yet there is not the least turn in the muscles or twist in the fibres of any one, which does not render them more proper for that particular animal's way of life than any other cast or texture of them would have been.

The most violent appetites in all creatures are *lust* and *hunger:* the first is a perpetual call upon them to propagate their kind; the latter to preserve themselves.

It is astonishing to consider the different degrees of care that descend from the parent to the young, so far as is absolutely necessary for the leaving a posterity. Some creatures cast their eggs as chance directs them, and think of them no farther; as insects and several kinds of fish: others, of a nicer frame, find out proper beds to deposit them in, and there leave them; as the serpent, the crocodile, and ostrich: others hatch their eggs and tend the birth, till it is able to shift for itself.

What can we call the principle which directs every different kind of bird to observe a particular plan in the structure of its nest, and directs all the same species to work after the same model? It cannot be *imitation;* for though you hatch a crow under a hen, and never let it see any of the works of its own kind, the nest it makes shall be the same, to the laying of a stick, with all the other nests of the same species. It cannot be *reason;* for were animals endued with it to as great a degree as man, their buildings would be as different as ours according to the different conveniences that they would propose to themselves.

Is it not remarkable that the same temper of weather, which raises this genial warmth in animals, should cover the trees with leaves, and the fields with grass, for their security and concealment, and produce such infinite swarms of insects for the support and sustenance of their respective broods?

Is it not wonderful that the love of the parent should be so violent while it lasts, and that it should last no longer than is necessary for the preservation of the young?

But notwithstanding this natural love in brutes is much more violent and intense than in rational creatures, Providence has taken care that it should be no longer troublesome to the parent than it is useful to the young; for so soon as the wants of the latter cease, the mother withdraws her fondness, and leaves them to provide for themselves; and, what is a very remarkable circumstance in this part of instinct, we find that the love of the parent may be lengthened out beyond its usual time, if the preservation of the species requires it: as we may see in birds that drive away their young as soon as they are able to get their livelihood, but continue to feed them if they are tied to the nest, or confined within a cage, or by any other means appear to be out of a condition of supplying their own necessities.

This natural love is not observed in animals to ascend from the young to the parent, which is not at all necessary for the continuance of the species: nor indeed in reasonable creatures does it rise in any proportion, as it spreads itself downwards; for, in all family affection, we find protection granted and favours bestowed are greater motives to love and tenderness, than safety, benefits, or life received.

One would wonder to hear sceptical men disputing for

the reason of animals, and telling us it is only our pride and prejudices that will not allow them the use of that faculty.

Reason shews itself in all occurrences of life; whereas the brute makes no discovery of such a talent but in what immediately regards his own preservation, or the continuance of his species. Animals in their generations are wiser than the sons of men; but their wisdom is confined to a few particulars, and lies in a very narrow compass. Take a brute out of his instinct, and you find him wholly deprived of understanding. To use an instance that comes often under observation:

With what caution does the hen provide herself a nest in places unfrequented, and free from noise and disturbance? When she has laid her eggs in such a manner that she can cover them, what care does she take in turning them frequently, that all parts may partake of the vital warmth? When she leaves them to provide for her necessary sustenance, how punctually does she return before they have time to cool, and become incapable of producing an animal? In the summer you see her giving herself greater freedoms, and quitting her care for above two hours together: but in winter, when the rigour of the season would chill the principles of life, and destroy the young one, she grows more assiduous in her attendance, and stays away but half the time. When the birth approaches, with how much nicety and attention does she help the chick to break its prison? Not to take notice of her covering it from the injuries of the weather, providing it proper nourishment, and teaching it to help itself; nor to mention her forsaking the nest, if after the usual time of reckoning the young one does not make its appearance. A chymical operation could not be followed with greater art or diligence, than is seen in the hatching of a chick; though there are many other birds that shew an infinitely greater sagacity in all the forementioned particulars.

But at the same time, the hen, that has all this seeming ingenuity (which is indeed absolutely necessary for the propagation of the species), considered in other respects, is without the least glimmerings of thought or common sense. She mistakes a piece of chalk for an egg, and sits upon it in the same manner: she is insensible of any increase or diminution in the number of those she lays: she does not distinguish between her own and those of another species, and when the birth appears of never so different a bird, will cherish it for her own. In all these circumstances, which do not carry an immediate regard to the subsistence of herself or her species, she is a very idiot.

There is not, in my opinion, anything more mysterious in nature than this instinct in animals, which thus rises above reason, and falls infinitely short of it. It cannot be accounted for by any properties in matter, and at the same time works after so odd a manner, that one cannot think it the faculty of an intellectual being. For my own part I look upon it as upon the principle of gravitation in bodies, which is not to be explained by any known qualities inherent in the bodies themselves, nor from the laws of mechanism, but, according to the best notions of the greatest philosophers, is an immediate impression from the first Mover, and the divine energy acting in the creatures.

L.

THE SAME SUBJECT, CONTINUED. [ADDISON.]

NO. 121. — THURSDAY, JULY 19, 1711.

JOVIS omnia plena. — VIRG. ECL. iii. 60.
ALL things are full of Jove.

As I was walking this morning in the great yard that belongs to my friend's country house, I was wonderfully pleased to see the different workings of instinct in a hen followed by a brood of ducks. The young, upon the sight of a pond, immediately ran into it; while the step-mother, with all imaginable anxiety, hovered about the borders of it, to call them out of an element that appeared to her so dangerous and destructive. As the different principle which acted in these different animals cannot be termed reason, so, when we call it *instinct*, we mean something we have no knowledge of. To me, as I hinted in my last paper, it seems the immediate direction of Providence, and such an operation of the Supreme Being as that which determines all the portions of matter to their proper centres. A modern philosopher, quoted by Monsieur Bayle, in his learned dissertation on the souls of brutes, delivers the same opinion, though in a bolder form of words, where he says, *Deus est anima brutorum*, God himself is the soul of brutes. Who can tell what to call that seeming sagacity in animals, which directs them to such food as is proper for them, and makes them naturally avoid whatever is noxious or unwholesome? Dampier, in his travels, tells us, that when seamen are thrown upon any of the unknown coasts of America, they never venture upon the fruit of any tree, how tempting soever it may appear, unless they observe that it is marked with the peckings of birds; but fall on without any fear or apprehension where the birds have been before them.

But notwithstanding animals have nothing like the use of reason, we find in them all the lower parts of our nature, the passions and senses, in their greatest strength and perfection. And here it is worth our observation, that all beasts and birds of prey are wonderfully subject to anger, malice, revenge and all the other violent passions that may animate them in search of their proper food; as those that are incapable of defending themselves, or annoying others, or whose safety lies chiefly in their flight, are suspicious, fearful, and apprehensive of every thing they see or hear; whilst others that are of assistance and use to man have their natures softened with something mild and tractable, and by that means are qualified for a domestic life. In this case the passions generally correspond with the make of the body. We do not find the fury of a lion in so weak and defenceless an animal as a lamb, nor the meekness of a lamb in a creature so armed for battle and assault as the lion. In the same manner, we find that particular animals have a more or less exquisite sharpness and sagacity in those particular senses which most turn to their advantage, and in which their safety and welfare is the most concerned.

Nor must we here omit that great variety of arms with which nature has differently fortified the bodies of several kinds of animals, such as claws, hoofs and horns, teeth, and tusks, a tail, a sting, a trunk, or a *proboscis*. It is likewise observed by naturalists, that it must be some hidden principle, distinct from what we call reason, which instructs animals in the use of these their arms, and teaches them to manage them to the best advantage; because they naturally defend themselves with that part in which their strength lies, before the weapon be formed in it: as is remarkable in lambs, which though they are bred within doors, and never saw the actions of their own species, push at those who approach them with their foreheads, before the first budding of a horn appears.

I shall add to these general observations an instance which Mr. Locke has given us of Providence, even in the imperfections of a creature which seems the meanest and most despicable in the whole animal world. "We may," says he, "from the make of an oyster, or cockle, conclude that it has not so many, nor so quick senses as a man, or several other animals; nor if it had, would it, in that state and incapacity of transferring itself from one place to another, be bettered by them. What good would sight and hearing do to a creature, that cannot move itself to or from the object, wherein at a distance it perceives good or evil? And would not quickness of sensation be an inconvenience to an animal that must be still where chance has once placed it, and there receive the afflux of colder or warmer, clean or foul water, as it happens to come to it?"

I shall add to this instance out of Mr. Locke another out of the learned Dr. More, who cites it from Cardan, in relation to another animal which Providence has left defective, but at the same time has shewn its wisdom in the formation of that organ in which it seems chiefly to have failed. "What is more obvious and ordinary than a mole? and yet what more palpable argument of Providence than she? the members of her body are so exactly fitted to her nature and manner of life; for her dwelling being under ground, where nothing is to be seen, nature has so obscurely fitted her with eyes, that naturalists can hardly agree whether she have any sight at all or no. But for amends, what she is capable of for her defence and warning of danger, she has very eminently conferred upon her; for she is exceeding quick of hearing. And then her short tail and short legs, but broad fore feet armed with sharp claws, we see by the event to what purpose they are, she so swiftly working herself under ground, and making her way so fast in the earth, as they that behold it cannot but admire it. Her legs therefore are short, that she need dig no more than will serve the mere thickness of her body; and her fore feet are broad that she may scoop away much earth at a time; and little or no tail she has, because she courses it not on the ground like the rat or the mouse, of whose kindred she is, but lives under the earth, and is fain to dig herself a dwelling there. And she making her way through so thick an element, which will not yield easily, as the air or the water, it had been dangerous to have drawn so long a train behind her; for her enemy might fall upon her rear, and fetch her out, before she had completed or got full possession of her works."

I cannot forbear mentioning Mr. Boyle's remark upon this last creature, who, I remember, somewhere in his works observes, that though the mole be not totally blind (as it is commonly thought) she has not sight enough to distinguish particular objects. Her eye is said to have but one humour in it, which is supposed to give her the idea of light, but of nothing else, and is so formed that this idea is probably painful to the animal. Whenever she comes up into broad day, she might be in danger of being taken, unless she were thus affected by a light striking upon her eye, and immediately warning her to bury herself in her proper element. More sight would be useless to her, as none at all might be fatal.

I have only instanced such animals as seem the most imperfect works of nature; and if Providence shews itself even in the blemishes of these creatures, how much more does it discover itself in the several endowments which it has variously bestowed upon such creatures as are more or less finished and completed in their several faculties, according to the condition of life in which they are posted.

I could wish our Royal Society would compile a body of natural history, the best that could be gathered together from books and observations. If the several writers among them took each his particular species, and gave us a distinct account of its original, birth, and education; its policies, hostilities, and alliances, with the frame and texture of its inward and outward parts, and particularly those that distinguish it from all other animals, with their peculiar aptitudes for the state of being in which Providence has placed them, it would be one of the best services their studies could do mankind, and not a little redound to the glory of the all-wise Contriver.

It is true such a natural history, after all the disquisitions of the learned, would be infinitely short and defective. Seas and deserts hide millions of animals from our observation. Innumerable artifices and stratagems are acted in the howling wilderness and in the great deep, that can never come to our knowledge. Besides that there are infinitely more species of creatures which are not to be seen without, nor indeed with the help of the finest glasses, than of such as are bulky enough for the naked eye to take hold of. However, from the consideration of such animals as lie within the compass of our knowledge, we might easily form a conclusion of the rest, that the same variety of wisdom and goodness runs through the whole creation, and puts every creature in a condition to provide for its safety and subsistence in its proper station.

Tully has given us an admirable sketch of natural history, in his second book concerning the Nature of the Gods; and that in a style so raised by metaphors and descriptions, that it lifts the subject above raillery and ridicule, which frequently fall on such observations when they pass through the hands of an ordinary writer.

L.

SIR ROGER AT THE ASSIZES. [ADDISON.]

NO. 122.—FRIDAY, JULY 20, 1711.

COMES jucundus in via pro vehiculo est.—PUB. SYR. FRAG.

AN agreeable companion upon the road is as good as a coach.

A MAN'S first care should be to avoid the reproaches of his own heart; his next, to escape the censures of the world: if the last interferes with the former, it ought to be entirely neglected; but otherwise there cannot be a greater satisfaction to an honest mind, than to see those approbations which it gives itself seconded by the applauses of the public: a man is more sure of conduct, when the verdict which he passes upon his own behaviour is thus warranted and confirmed by the opinion of all that know him.

My worthy friend Sir Roger is one of those who is not only at peace within himself, but beloved and esteemed by all about him. He receives a suitable tribute for his universal benevolence to mankind, in the returns of affection and good-will, which are paid him by every one that lives within his neighbourhood. I lately met with two or three odd instances of that general respect which is shewn to the good old knight. He would needs carry Will Wimble and myself with him to the county assizes: as we were upon the road Will Wimble joined a couple of plain men who rode before us, and conversed with them for some time; during which my friend Sir Roger acquainted me with their characters.

"The first of them," says he, "that has a spaniel by his side, is a yeoman of about an hundred pounds a year, an honest man: he is just within the game-act, and qualified to kill an hare or a pheasant: he knocks down his dinner with his gun twice or thrice a week: and by that means lives much cheaper than those who have not so good an estate as himself. He would be a good neighbour if he did not destroy so many partridges: in short he is a very sensible man; shoots flying; and has been several times foreman of the petty jury.

"That other that rides along with him is Tom Touchy, a fellow famous for taking the law of everybody. There is not one in the town where he lives that he has not sued at a quarter-sessions. The rogue had once the impudence to go to law with the widow. His head is full of costs, damages, and ejectments: he plagued a couple of honest gentlemen so long for a trespass in breaking one of his hedges, till he was forced to sell the ground it enclosed to defray the charges of the prosecution: his father left him fourscore pounds a year; but he has cast and been cast so often, that he is not now worth thirty. I suppose he is going upon the old business of the willow tree."

As Sir Roger was giving me this account of Tom Touchy, Will Wimble and his two companions stopped short till he came up to them. After having paid their respects to Sir Roger, Will told him that Mr. Touchy and he must appeal to him upon a dispute that arose between them. Will it seems had been giving his fellow-traveller an account of his angling one day in such a hole; when Tom Touchy, instead of hearing out his story, told him that Mr. such-a-one, if he pleased, might *take the law of him* for fishing in that part of the river. My friend Sir Roger heard them both upon a round trot; and after having paused some time, told them, with the air of a man who would not give his judgment rashly, that *much might be said on both sides.* They were neither of them dissatisfied with the knight's determination, because neither of them found himself in the wrong by it: upon which we made the best of our way to the assizes.

The court was set before Sir Roger came; but notwithstanding all the justices had taken their places upon the bench, they made room for the old knight at the head of them; who, for his reputation in the country, took occasion to whisper in the judge's ear, *that he was glad his lordship had met with so much good weather in his circuit.* I was listening to the proceedings of the court with much attention, and infinitely pleased with that great appearance of solemnity which so properly accompanies such a public administration of our laws; when, after about an hour's sitting, I observed to my great surprise, in the midst of a trial, that my friend Sir Roger was getting up to speak. I was in some pain for him till I found he had acquitted himself of two or three sentences, with a look of much business and great intrepidity.

Upon his first rising the court was hushed, and a general whisper ran among the country people that Sir Roger *was up*. The speech he made was so little to the purpose, that I shall not trouble my readers with an account of it; and I believe was not so much designed by the knight himself to inform the court, as to give him a figure in my eye, and keep up his credit in the country.

I was highly delighted, when the court rose, to see the gentlemen of the country gathering about my old friend, and striving who should compliment him most; at the same time that the ordinary people gazed upon him at a distance, not a little admiring his courage, that was not afraid to speak to the judge.

In our return home we met with a very odd accident; which I cannot forbear relating, because it shews how desirous all who know Sir Roger are of giving him marks of their esteem. When we were arrived upon the verge of his estate, we stopped at a little inn to rest ourselves and our horses. The man of the house had, it seems, been formerly a servant in the knight's family; and to do honour to his old master, had some time since, unknown to Sir Roger, put him up in a sign-post before the door; so that "the Knight's Head" had hung out upon the road about a week before he himself knew anything of the matter. As soon as Sir Roger was acquainted with it, finding that his servant's indiscretion proceeded wholly from affection and good-will, he only told him that he had made him too high a compliment; and when the fellow seemed to think that could hardly be, added with a more decisive look, that it was too great an honour for any man under a duke; but told him at the same time, that it might be altered with a very few touches, and that he himself would be at the charge of it. Accordingly they got a painter by the knight's directions to add a pair of whiskers to the face, and by a little aggravation of the features to change it into the *Saracen's Head.* I should not have known this story, had not the inn-keeper, upon Sir Roger's alighting, told him in my hearing, that his honour's head was brought back last night with the alterations that he had ordered to be made in it. Upon this my friend with his usual cheerfulness related the particulars above-mentioned, and ordered the head to be brought into the room. I could not forbear discovering greater expressions of mirth than ordinary upon the appearance of this monstrous face, under which, notwithstanding it was made to frown and stare in a most extraordinary manner, I could still discover a distant resemblance of my old friend. Sir Roger, upon seeing me laugh, desired me to tell him truly if I thought it possible for people to know him in that disguise. I at first kept my usual silence: but upon the knight's conjuring me to tell him whether it was not still more like himself than a Saracen, I composed my countenance in the best manner I could, and replied *That much might be said on both sides.*

These several adventures, with the knight's behaviour in them, gave me as pleasant a day as ever I met with in any of my travels. L.

A STORY OF EUDOXUS AND LEONTINE.

[ADDISON.]

NO. 123.—SATURDAY, JULY 21, 1711.

DOCTRINA sed vim promovet insitam,
Rectique cultus pectora roborant;
Utcunque defecere mores,
Dedecorant bene nata culpæ.—HOR. LIB. 4, OD. iv. 33.

YET the best blood by learning is refin'd,
And virtue arms the solid mind;
Whilst vice will stain the noblest race,
And the paternal stamp efface.—OLDISWORTH.

As I was yesterday taking the air with my friend Sir Roger, we were met by a fresh-coloured ruddy young man, who rid by us full speed, with a couple of servants behind him. Upon my inquiry who he was, Sir Roger told me that he was a young gentleman of considerable estate, who had been educated by a tender mother that lived not many miles from the place where we were. She is a very good lady, says my friend, but took so much care of her son's health that she has made him good for nothing. She quickly found that reading was bad for his eyes, and that writing made his head ake. He was let loose among the woods as soon as he was able to ride on horseback, or to carry a gun upon his shoulder. To be brief, I found, by my friend's account of him, that he had got a great stock of health, but nothing else; and that if it were a man's business only to live, there would not be a more accomplished young fellow in the whole country.

The truth of it is, since my residing in these parts I have seen and heard innumerable instances of young heirs and elder brothers, who either from their own reflecting upon the estates they are born to, and therefore thinking all other accomplishments unnecessary, or from hearing these notions frequently inculcated to them by the flattery of their servants and domestics, or from the same foolish thought prevailing in those who have the care of their education, are of no manner of use but to keep up their families, and transmit their lands and houses in a line to posterity.

This makes me often think on a story I have heard of two friends, which I shall give my reader at large, under feigned names. The moral of it may, I hope, be useful, though there are some circumstances which make it rather appear like a novel, than a true story.

Eudoxus and Leontine began the world with small estates. They were both of them men of good sense and great virtue. They prosecuted their studies together in their earlier years, and entered into such a friendship as lasted to the end of their lives. Eudoxus, at his first setting out in the world, threw himself into a court, where by his natural endowments and his acquired abilities he made his way from one post to another, till at length he had raised a very considerable fortune. Leontine on the contrary sought all opportunities of improving his mind by study, conversation, and travel. He was not only acquainted with all the sciences, but with the most eminent professors of them throughout Europe. He knew perfectly well the interest of its princes, with the customs and fashions of their courts, and could scarce meet with the name of an extraordinary person in the Gazette, whom he had not either talked to or seen. In short, he had so well mixed and digested his knowledge of men and books, that he made one of the most accomplished persons of his age. During the whole course of his studies and travels he kept up a punctual correspondence with Eudoxus, who often made himself acceptable to the principal men about court by the intelligence which he received from Leontine. When they were both turned of forty (an age in which, according to Mr. Cowley, *there is no dallying with life*,) they determined, pursuant to the resolution they had taken in the beginning of their lives, to retire, and pass the remainder of their days in the country. In order to do this, they both of them married much about the same time. Leontine, with his own and his wife's fortune, bought a farm of three hundred a year, which lay within the neighbourhood of his friend Eudoxus, who had purchased an estate of as many thousands. They were both of them fathers about the same time, Eudoxus having a son born to him, and Leontine, a daughter; but to the unspeakable grief of the latter, his young wife (in whom all his happiness was wrapt up) died in a few days after the birth of her daughter. His affliction would have been insupportable, had not he been comforted by the daily visits and conversations of his friend. As they were one day talking together with their usual intimacy, Leontine, considering how incapable he was of giving his daughter a proper education in his own house, and Eudoxus reflecting on the ordinary behaviour of a son who knows himself to be the heir of a great estate, they both agreed upon an exchange of children, namely, that the boy should be bred up with Leontine as his son, and that the girl should live with Eudoxus as his daughter, till they were each of them arrived at years of discretion. The wife of Eudoxus, knowing that her son could not be so advantageously brought up as under the care of Leontine, and considering at the same time that he would be perpetually under her own eye, was by degrees prevailed upon to fall in with the project. She therefore took Leonilla, for that was the name of the girl, and educated her as her own daughter. The two friends on each side had wrought themselves to such an habitual tenderness for the children who were under their direction, that each of them had the real passion of a father, where the title was but imaginary. Florio, the name of the young heir that lived with Leontine, though he had all the duty and affection imaginable for his supposed parent, was taught to rejoice at the sight of Eudoxus, who visited his friend very frequently, and was dictated by his natural affection, as well as by the rules of prudence, to make himself esteemed and beloved by Florio. The boy was now old enough to know his supposed father's circumstances, and that therefore he was to make his way in the world by his own industry. This consideration grew stronger in him every day, and produced so good an effect, that he applied himself with more than ordinary attention to the pursuit of every thing which Leontine recommended to him. His natural abilities, which were very good, assisted by the directions of so excellent a counsellor, enabled him to make a quicker progress than ordinary through all the parts of his education. Before he was twenty years of age, having finished his studies and exercises with great applause, he was removed from the university to the Inns of Court, where there are very few that make themselves considerable proficients in the study of the place, who know they shall arrive at great estates without them. This was not Florio's case; he found that three hundred a year was but a poor estate for Leontine and himself to live upon; so that he studied without intermission, till he gained a very good insight into the constitution and laws of his country.

I should have told my reader, that whilst Florio lived at the house of his foster-father, he was always an acceptable guest in the family of Eudoxus, where he became acquainted with Leonilla from her infancy. His acquaintance with her by degrees grew into love, which in a mind trained up in all the sentiments of honour and virtue became a very uneasy passion. He despaired of gaining an heiress of so great a fortune, and would rather have died than attempted it by any indirect methods. Leonilla, who was a woman of the greatest beauty, joined with the greatest modesty, entertained at the same time a secret passion for Florio, but conducted herself with so much prudence that she never gave him the least intimation of it. Florio was now engaged in all those arts and improvements that are proper to raise a man's private fortune, and give him a figure in his country, but secretly tormented with that passion, which burns with the greatest fury in a virtuous and noble heart, when he received a sudden summons from Leontine, to repair to him in the country the next day. For it seems Eudoxus was so filled with the report of his son's reputation, that he could no longer withhold making himself known to him. The morning after his arrival at the house of his supposed father, Leontine told him that Eudoxus had something of great importance to communicate to him ; upon which the good man embraced him and wept. Florio was no sooner arrived at the great house that stood in his neighbourhood, but Eudoxus took him by the hand, after the first salutes were over, and conducted him into his closet. He there opened to him the whole secret of his parentage and education, concluding after this manner: "I have no other way of acknowledging my gratitude to Leontine, than by marrying you to his daughter. He shall not lose the pleasure of being your father by the discovery I have made to you. Leonilla too shall be still my daughter; her filial piety, though misplaced, has been so exemplary, that it deserves the greatest reward I can confer upon it. You shall have the pleasure of seeing a great estate fall to you, which you would have lost the relish of, had you known yourself born to it. Continue only to deserve it in the same manner you did before you were possessed of it. I have left your mother in the next room. Her heart yearns towards you. She is making the same discoveries to Leonilla which I have made to yourself." Florio was so overwhelmed with this profusion of happiness, that he was not able to make a reply, but threw himself down at his father's feet, and amidst a flood of tears kissed and embraced his knees, asking his blessing, and expressing in dumb shew those sentiments of love, duty, and gratitude, that were too big for utterance. To conclude, the happy pair were married, and half Eudoxus's estate settled upon them. Leontine and Eudoxus passed the remainder of their lives together, and received in the dutiful and affectionate behaviour of Florio and Leonilla the just recompense, as well as the natural effects, of that care which they had bestowed upon them in their education.

L.

THE SPECTATOR ON PARTY-SPIRIT. [ADDISON.]

No. 125. — TUESDAY, JULY 24, 1711.

> NE pueri, ne tanta animis assuescite bella:
> Neu patriæ validas in viscera vertite vires. — VIRG. ÆN. vi. 832.
>
> EMBRACE again, my sons, be foes no more,
> Nor stain your country with her children's gore. — DRYDEN.

MY worthy friend Sir Roger, when we are talking of the malice of parties, very frequently tells us an accident that happened to him when he was a school-boy, which was at a time when the feuds ran high between the round-heads and cavaliers. This worthy knight, being then but a stripling, had occasion to inquire which was the way to St. Anne's Lane; upon which the person whom he spoke to, instead of answering his question, called him a young Popish cur, and asked him who had made Anne a saint! The boy, being in some confusion, inquired of the next he met, which was the way to Anne's Lane; but was called a prick-eared cur for his pains, and instead of being shewn the way, was told that she had been a saint before he was born, and would be one after he was hanged. Upon this, says Sir Roger, I did not think fit to repeat the former questions, but going into every lane of the neighbourhood, asked what they called the name of that lane. By which ingenious artifice he found out the place he inquired after, without giving offence to any party. Sir Roger generally closes this narrative with reflexions on the mischief that parties do in the country; how they spoil good neighbourhood, and make honest gentlemen hate one another; besides that they manifestly tend to the prejudice of the land-tax, and the destruction of the game.

There cannot a greater judgment befal a country than such a dreadful spirit of division as rends a government into two distinct people, and makes them greater strangers and more averse to one another, than if they were actually two different nations. The effects of such a division are pernicious to the last degree, not only with regard to those advantages which they give the common enemy, but to those private evils which they produce in the heart of almost every particular person. This influence is very fatal both to men's morals and their understandings; it sinks the virtue of a nation, and not only so, but destroys even common sense.

A furious party-spirit, when it rages in its full violence, exerts itself in civil war and bloodshed; and when it is under its greatest restraints, naturally breaks out in falsehood, detraction, calumny, and a partial administration of justice. In a word, it fills a nation with spleen and rancour, and extinguishes all the seeds of good-nature, compassion, and humanity.

Plutarch says very finely, that a man should not allow himself to hate even his enemies, because, says he, "if you indulge this passion on some occasions, it will rise of itself in others; if you hate your enemies, you will contract such a vicious habit of mind, as by degrees will break out upon those who are your friends, or those who are indifferent to you." I might here observe how admirably this precept of morality (which derives the malignity of hatred from the passion itself, and not from its object) answers to that great rule which was dictated to the world about an hundred years before this philosopher wrote; but instead of that, I shall only take notice, with a real grief of heart, that the minds of many good men among us appear soured with party-principles, and alienated from one another in such a manner, as seems to me altogether inconsistent with the dictates either of reason or religion. Zeal for a public cause is apt to breed passions in the hearts of virtuous persons, to which the regard of their own private interest would never have betrayed them.

If this party-spirit has so ill an effect on our morals, it has likewise a very great one upon our judgments. We often hear a poor insipid paper or pamphlet cried up, and sometimes a noble piece depreciated, by those who are of a different principle from the author. One who is actuated by this spirit is almost under an incapacity of discerning either real blemishes or beauties. A man of merit in a different principle, is like an object seen in two different mediums, that appears crooked or broken, however straight and entire it may be in itself. For this reason there is scarce a person of any figure in England who does not go by two contrary characters, as opposite to one another as light and darkness. Knowledge and learning suffer in a particular manner from this strange prejudice, which at present prevails amongst all ranks and degrees in the British nation. As men formerly became eminent in learned societies by their parts and acquisitions, they now distinguish themselves by the warmth and violence with which they espouse their respective parties. Books are valued upon the like considerations: an abusive scurrilous style passes for satire, and a dull scheme of party notions is called fine writing.

There is one piece of sophistry practised by both sides, and that is the taking any scandalous story, that has been ever whispered or invented of a private man, for a known undoubted truth, and raising suitable speculations upon it. Calumnies that have been never proved, or have been often refuted, are the ordinary postulatums of these infamous scribblers, upon which they proceed as upon first principles granted by all men, though in their hearts they know they are false, or at best very doubtful. When they have laid these foundations of scurrility, it is no wonder that their superstructure is every way answerable to them. If this shameless practice of the present age endures much longer, praise and reproach will cease to be motives of action in good men.

There are certain periods of time in all governments when this inhuman spirit prevails. Italy was long torn to pieces by the Guelfes and Gibellines, and France by those who were for and against the League: but it is very unhappy for a man to be born in such a stormy and tempestuous season. It is the restless ambition of artful men, that thus breaks a people into factions, and draws several well-meaning persons to their interest by a specious concern for their country. How many honest minds are filled with uncharitable and barbarous notions, out of their zeal for the public good? What cruelties and outrages would they not commit against men of an adverse party, whom they would honour and esteem, if instead of considering them as they are represented, they knew them as they are? Thus are persons of the greatest probity seduced into shameful errors and prejudices, are made bad men even by that noblest of principles, the love of their country. I cannot here forbear mentioning the famous Spanish proverb, *If there were neither fools nor knaves in the world all people would be of one mind.*

For my own part, I could heartily wish that all honest men would enter into an association, for the support of one another against the endeavours of those whom they ought to look upon as their common enemies, whatsoever side they may belong to. Were there such an honest body of neutral forces, we should never see the worst of men in great figures of life, because they are useful to a party; nor the best unregarded, because they are above practising those methods which would be grateful to their faction. We should then single every criminal out of the herd, and hunt him down however formidable and overgrown he might appear: on the contrary, we should shelter distressed innocence, and defend virtue, however beset with contempt or ridicule, envy or defamation. In short, we should not any longer regard our fellow-subjects as Whigs or Tories, but should make the man of merit our friend, and the villain our enemy.

C.

SIR ROGER AND POLITICS. [Addison.]

No. 126. Wednesday, July 25, 1711.

Tros Rutulusve fuat, nullo discrimine habebo. — Virg. Æn. x. 108.

Rutulians, Trojans, are the same to me. — Dryden.

In my yesterday's paper I proposed, that the honest men of all parties should enter into a kind of association for the defence of one another, and the confusion of their common enemies. As it is designed this neutral body should act with a regard to nothing but truth and equity, and divest themselves of the little heats and prepossessions that cleave to parties of all kinds, I have prepared for them the following form of an association, which may express their intentions in the most plain and simple manner.

We whose names are hereunto subscribed, do solemnly declare, that we do in our consciences believe two and two make four; and that we shall adjudge any man whatsoever to be our enemy who endeavours to persuade us to the contrary. We are likewise ready to maintain with the hazard of all that is near and dear to us, that six is less than seven in all times and all places; and that ten will not be more three years hence than it is at present. We do also firmly declare, that it is our resolution as long as we live to call black black, and white white. And we shall upon all occasions oppose such persons that upon any day of the year shall call black white, or white black, with the utmost peril of our lives and fortunes.

Were there such a combination of honest men, who without any regard to places would endeavour to extirpate all such furious zealots as would sacrifice one half of their country to the passion and interest of the other; as also such infamous hypocrites, that are for promoting their own advantage under colour of the public good; with all the profligate immoral retainers to each side, that have nothing to recommend them but an implicit submission to their leaders; we should soon see that furious party-spirit extinguished, which may in time expose us to the derision and contempt of all the nations about us.

A member of this society, that would thus carefully employ himself in making room for merit, by throwing down the worthless and depraved part of mankind from those conspicuous stations of life to which they have been sometimes advanced, and all this without any regard to his private interest, would be no small benefactor to his country.

I remember to have read in Diodorus Siculus an account of a very active little animal, which I think he calls the Ichneumon, that makes it the whole business of his life to break the eggs of the crocodile, which he is always in search after. This instinct is the more remarkable, because the Ichneumon never feeds upon the eggs he has broken, nor any other way finds his account in them. Were it not for the incessant labours of this industrious animal, Egypt, says the historian, would be over-run with crocodiles; for the Egyptians are so far from destroying those pernicious creatures, that they worship them as gods.

If we look into the behaviour of ordinary partisans, we shall find them far from resembling this disinterested animal; and rather acting after the example of the wild Tartars, who are ambitious of destroying a man of the most extraordinary parts and accomplishments, as thinking that upon his decease, the same talents, whatever post they qualified him for, enter of course into his destroyer.

As in the whole train of my speculations I have endeavoured as much as I am able to extinguish that pernicious spirit of passion and prejudice, which rages with the same violence in all parties, I am still the more desirous of doing some good in this particular, because I observe that the spirit of party reigns more in the country than in the town. It here contracts a kind of brutality and rustic fierceness, to which men of a politer conversation are wholly strangers. It extends itself even to the return of the bow and the hat; and at the same time that the heads of parties preserve towards one another an outward shew of good breeding, and keep up a perpetual intercourse of civilities, their tools that are dispersed in these outlying parts will not so much as mingle together at a cock-match. This humour fills the country with several periodical meetings of Whig jockeys and Tory fox-hunters; not to mention the innumerable curses, frowns, and whispers it produces at a quarter-sessions.

I do not know whether I have observed in any of my former papers, that my friends Sir Roger de Coverley and Sir Andrew Freeport are of different principles, the first of them inclined to the *landed* and the other to the *monied* interest. This humour is so moderate in each of them, that it proceeds no farther than to an agreeable raillery, which very often diverts the rest of the club. I find however that the knight is a much stronger Tory in the country than in town, which as he has told me in my ear, is absolutely necessary for the keeping up his interest. In all our journey from London to his house we did not so much as bait at a Whig inn; or if by chance the coach-man stopped at a wrong place, one of Sir Roger's servants would ride up to his master full speed, and whisper to him that the master of the house was against such an one in the last election. This often betrayed us into hard beds and bad cheer; for we were not so inquisitive about the inn as the inn-keeper; and provided our landlord's principles were sound, did not take any notice of the staleness of his provisions. This I found still the more inconvenient, because the better the host was, the worse generally were his accommodations; the fellow knowing very well that those who were his friends would take up with coarse diet and hard lodging. For these reasons, all the while I was upon the road I dreaded entering into an house of any one that Sir Roger had applauded for an honest man.

Since my stay at Sir Roger's in the country, I daily find more instances of this narrow party-humour. Being upon a bowling-green at a neighbouring market-town the other day, (for that is the place where the gentlemen of one side meet once a week,) I observed a stranger among them of a better presence and genteeler behaviour than ordinary; but was much surprised, that notwithstanding he was a very fair better, nobody would take him up. But upon inquiry I found, that he was one who had given a disagreeable vote in a former parliament, for which reason there was not a man upon that bowling-green who would have so much correspondence with him as to win his money of him.

Among other instances of this nature, I must not omit one which concerns myself. Will Wimble was the other day relating several strange stories that he had picked up, nobody knows where, of a certain great man; and upon my staring at him, as one that was surprised to hear such things in the country, which had never been so much as whispered in the town, Will stopped short in the thread of his discourse, and after dinner asked my friend Sir Roger in his ear, if he was sure that I was not a fanatic.

It gives me a serious concern to see such a spirit of dissension in the country; not only as it destroys virtue and common sense, and renders us in a manner barbarians towards one another, but as it perpetuates our animosities, widens our breaches, and transmits our present passions and prejudices to our posterity. For my own part, I am sometimes afraid that I discover the seeds of a civil war in these our divisions; and therefore cannot but bewail, as in their first principles, the miseries and calamities of our children.

C.

SIR ROGER AND THE GIPSIES. [ADDISON.]

NO. 130.—MONDAY, JULY 30, 1711.

SEMPERQUE recentes
Convectare juvat prædas, et vivere rapto.
— VIRG. ÆN. vii. 748.

HUNTING their sport, and plundering was their trade. — DRYDEN.

As I was yesterday riding out in the fields with my friend Sir Roger, we saw at a little distance from us a troop of gipsies. Upon the first discovery of them, my friend was in some doubt whether he should not exert the *Justice of the peace* upon such a band of lawless vagrants; but not having his clerk with him, who is a necessary counsellor on those occasions, and fearing that his poultry might fare the worse for it, he let the thought drop: but at the same time gave me a particular account of the mischiefs they do in the country, in stealing people's goods and spoiling their servants. "If a stray piece of linen hangs upon an hedge," says Sir Roger, "they are sure to have it; if a hog loses his way in the fields, it is ten to one but he becomes their prey; our geese cannot live in peace for them: if a man prosecutes them with severity, his henroost is sure to pay for it. They generally straggle into these parts about this time of the year; and set the heads of our servant-maids so agog for husbands, that we do not expect to have any business done as it should be whilst they are in the country. I have an honest dairy-maid who crosses their hands with a piece of silver every summer, and never fails being promised the handsomest young fellow in the parish for her pains. Your friend the butler has been fool enough to be seduced by them; and though he is sure to lose a knife, a fork, or a spoon every time his fortune is told him, generally shuts himself up in the pantry with an old gypsy for above half an hour once in a twelvemonth. Sweet-hearts are the things they live upon, which they bestow very plentifully upon all those that apply themselves to them. You see now and then some handsome young jades among them: the sluts have very often white teeth and black eyes."

Sir Roger observing that I listened with great attention to his account of a people who were so entirely new to me, told me, that if I would they should tell us our fortunes. As I was very well pleased with the knight's proposal, we rid up and communicated our hands to them. A Cassandra of the crew, after having examined my lines very diligently, told me, that I loved a pretty maid in a corner, that I was a good woman's man, with some other particulars which I do not think proper to relate. My friend Sir Roger alighted from his horse, and exposing his palm to two or three of them that stood by him, they crumpled it into all shapes, and diligently scanned every wrinkle that could be made in it; when one of them who was elder and more sun-burnt than the rest, told him, that he had a widow in his line of life; upon which the knight cried, "Go, go, you are an idle baggage"; and at the same time smiled upon me. The gipsy finding he was not displeased in his heart, told him after a farther inquiry into his hand, that his true love was constant, and that she should dream of him to-night: my old friend cried "Pish," and bid her go on. The gipsy told him that he was a bachelor, but would not be so long; and that he was dearer to somebody than he thought; the knight still repeated that she was an idle baggage, and bid her go on. "Ah, master," said the gipsy, "that roguish leer of yours makes a pretty woman's heart ake; you han't that simper about the mouth for nothing." The uncouth gibberish with which all this was uttered, like the darkness of an oracle, made us the more attentive to it. To be short, the knight left the money with her that he had crossed her hand with, and got up again on his horse.

As we were riding away, Sir Roger told me, that he knew several sensible people who believed these gipsies now and then foretold very strange things; and for half an hour together appeared more jocund than ordinary. In the height of his good humour, meeting a common beggar upon the road who was no conjurer, as he went to relieve him, he found his pocket was picked; that being a kind of palmistry at which this race of vermin are very dexterous.

I might here entertain my reader with historical remarks on this idle profligate people, who infest all the countries in Europe, and live in the midst of governments in a kind of commonwealth by themselves. But instead of entering into observations of this nature, I shall fill the remaining part of my paper with a story which is still fresh in Holland, and was printed in one of our monthly accounts about twenty years ago. "As the Trekschuyt, or the hackney boat, which carries passengers from Leyden to Amsterdam, was putting off, a boy running along the side of the canal desired to be taken in; which the master of the boat refused, because the lad had not quite money enough to pay the usual fare. An eminent merchant being pleased with the looks of the boy, and secretly touched with compassion towards him, paid the money for him, and ordered him to be taken on board. Upon talking with him afterwards, he found that he could speak readily in three or four languages, and learned upon further examination that he had been stolen away when he was a child by a gipsy, and had rambled ever since with a gang of these strollers up and down several parts of Europe. It happened that the merchant, whose heart seems to have inclined towards the boy by a secret kind of instinct, had himself lost a child some years before. The parents after a long search for him, gave him up for drowned in one of the canals with which that country abounds; and the mother was so afflicted at the loss of a fine boy, who was her only son, that she died for grief of it. Upon laying together all particulars, and examining the several moles and marks by which the mother used to describe the child when he was first missing, the boy proved to be the son of the merchant whose heart had so unaccountably melted at the sight of him. The lad was very well pleased to find a father who was so rich, and likely to leave him a good estate: the father on the other hand was not a little delighted to see a son return to him, whom he had given up for lost, with such a strength of constitution, sharpness of understanding, and skill of languages." Here the printed story leaves off, but if I may give credit to reports, our linguist, having received such extraordinary rudiments towards a good education, was afterwards trained up in everything that becomes a gentleman; wearing off by little and little all the vicious habits and practices that he had been used to in the course of his peregrinations; nay, it is said, that he has since been employed in foreign courts upon national business, with great reputation to himself and honour to those who sent him, and that he has visited several countries as a public minister, in which he formerly wandered as a gipsy.

C.

A SUMMONS TO LONDON.

No. 131. — Tuesday, July 31, 1711.

Ipsæ rursum concedite sylvæ. — Virg. Ec. x. 63.

Once more, ye woods, adieu.

It is usual for a man who loves country sports to preserve the game on his own grounds, and divert himself upon those that belong to his neighbour. My friend Sir Roger generally goes two or three miles from his house, and gets into the frontiers of his estate, before he beats about in search of a hare or partridge, on purpose to spare his own fields, where he is always sure of finding diversion when the worst comes to the worst. By this means the breed about his house has time to increase and multiply, besides that the sport is the more agreeable where the game is the harder to come at, and where it does not lie so thick as to produce any perplexity or confusion in the pursuit. For these reasons the country gentleman, like the fox, seldom preys near his own home.

In the same manner I have made a month's excursion out of town, which is the great field of game for sportsmen of my species, to try my fortune in the country, where I have started several subjects, and hunted them down, with some pleasure to myself, and I hope to others. I am here forced to use a great deal of diligence before I can spring anything to my mind, whereas in town, whilst

London through an Arch of London Bridge

By the Italian artist, Canaletto. The dome of St. Paul's at the right. (*From the collection of Mr. H. Oppenheim.*)

THE PARADE, ST. JAMES'S PARK

Where the sparks and toasts promenaded. Few comedies of the time fail to mention this section of the West End. (*Boston Museum of Fine Arts.*)

I am following one character, it is ten to one but I am crossed in my way by another, and put up such a variety of odd creatures in both sexes, that they foil the scent of one another, and puzzle the chase. My greatest difficulty in the country is to find sport, and in town to choose it. In the mean time, as I have given a whole month's rest to the cities of London and Westminster, I promise myself abundance of new game upon my return thither.

It is indeed high time for me to leave the country, since I find the whole neighbourhood begin to grow very inquisitive after my name and character; my love of solitude, taciturnity, and particular way of life, having raised a great curiosity in all these parts.

The notions which have been framed of me are various; some look upon me as very proud, some as very modest, and some as very melancholy. Will Wimble, as my friend the butler tells me, observing me very much alone, and extremely silent when I am in company, is afraid I have killed a man. The country people seem to suspect me for a conjurer; and some of them hearing of the visit which I made to Moll White, will needs have it that Sir Roger has brought down a cunning man with him, to cure the old woman, and free the country from her charms. So that the character which I go under in part of the neighbourhood, is what they here call a *white witch.*

A justice of peace, who lives about five miles off, and is not of Sir Roger's party, has, it seems, said twice or thrice at his table, that he wishes Sir Roger does not harbour a Jesuit in his house; and that he thinks the gentlemen of the country would do very well to make me give some account of myself.

On the other side, some of Sir Roger's friends are afraid the old knight is imposed upon by a designing fellow, and as they have heard that he converses very promiscuously when he is in town, do not know but he has brought down with him some discarded Whig, that is sullen, and says nothing because he is out of place.

Such is the variety of opinions which are here entertained of me, so that I pass among some for a disaffected person, and among others for a popish priest; among some for a wizard, and among others for a murderer; and all this for no other reason, that I can imagine, but because I do not hoot, and hollow, and make a noise. It is true, my friend Sir Roger tells them that it is my way, and that I am only a philosopher; but this will not satisfy them. They think there is more in me than he discovers, and that I do not hold my tongue for nothing.

For these and other reasons I shall set out for London to-morrow, having found by experience that the country is not a place for a person of my temper, who does not love jollity, and what they call good neighbourhood. A man that is out of humour when an unexpected guest breaks in upon him, and does not care for sacrificing an afternoon to every chance comer, — that will be the master of his own time, and the pursuer of his own inclinations, — makes but a very unsociable figure in this kind of life. I shall therefore retire into the town, if I may make use of that phrase, and get into the crowd again as fast as I can, in order to be alone. I can there raise what speculations I please upon others without being observed myself, and at the same time enjoy all the advantages of company with all the privileges of solitude. In the meanwhile, to finish the month, and conclude these my rural speculations, I shall here insert a letter from my friend Will Honeycomb, who has not lived a month for these forty years out of the smoke of London, and rallies me after his way upon my country life.

"DEAR SPEC,

"I suppose this letter will find thee picking up daisies, or smelling to a lock of hay, or passing away thy time in some innocent country diversion of the like nature. I have however orders from the club to summon thee up to town, being all of us cursedly afraid thou wilt not be able to relish our company, after thy conversations with Moll White and Will Wimble. Pr'ythee don't send up any more stories of a cock and a bull, nor frighten the town with spirits and witches. Thy speculations begin to smell confoundedly of woods and meadows. If thou dost not come up quickly, we shall conclude that thou art in love with one of Sir Roger's dairy-maids. Service to the knight. Sir Andrew is grown the cock of the club since he left us, and if he does not return quickly, will make every mother's son of us commonwealth's men.

"Dear Spec,

"Thine eternally,

"WILL HONEYCOMB."

C.

THE JOURNEY TO LONDON. [STEELE.]

NO. 132. — WEDNESDAY, AUGUST 1, 1711.

QUI, aut tempus quid postulet non videt, aut plura loquitur, aut se ostentat, aut eorum quibuscum est rationem non habet, is ineptus esse dicitur. — TULL.

THAT man may be called impertinent, who considers not the circumstances of time, or engrosses the conversation, or makes himself the subject of his discourse, or pays no regard to the company he is in.

HAVING notified to my good friend Sir Roger that I should set out for London the next day, his horses were ready at the appointed hour in the evening; and attended by one of his grooms, I arrived at the county-town at twilight, in order to be ready for the stage-coach the day following. As soon as we arrived at the inn, the servant who waited upon me inquired of the chamberlain in my hearing what company he had for the coach? The fellow answered, "Mrs. Betty Arable, the great fortune, and the widow her mother; a recruiting officer (who took a place because they were to go); young 'Squire Quickset, her cousin (that her mother wished her to be married to); Ephraim the Quaker, her guardian; and a gentleman that had studied himself dumb from Sir Roger de Coverley's." I observed by what he said of myself, that according to his office he dealt much in intelligence; and doubted not but there was some foundation for his reports of the rest of the company, as well as for the whimsical account he gave of me. The next morning at day-break we were all called; and I, who know my own natural shyness, and endeavour to be as little liable to be disputed with as possible, dressed immediately, that I might make no one wait. The first preparation for our setting out was, that the captain's half-pike was placed near the coachman, and a drum behind the coach. In the mean time the drummer, the captain's equipage, was very loud, "that none of the captain's things should be placed so as to be spoiled;" upon which his cloak-bag was fixed in the seat of the coach; and the captain himself, according to a frequent, though invidious behaviour of military men, ordered his man to look sharp, that none but one of the ladies should have the place he had taken fronting the coach-box.

We were in some little time fixed in our seats, and sat with that dislike which people not too good-natured usually conceive of each other at first sight. The coach jumbled us insensibly into some sort of familiarity: and we had not moved above two miles, when the widow asked the captain what success he had in his recruiting? The officer, with a frankness he believed very graceful, told her, "that indeed he had but very little luck, and had suffered much by desertion, therefore should be glad to end his warfare in the service of her or her fair daughter. In a word," continued he, "I am a soldier, and to be plain is my character: you see me, Madam, young, sound, and impudent; take me yourself, widow, or give me to her, I will be wholly at your disposal. I am a soldier of fortune, ha!"—This was followed by a vain laugh of his own, and a deep silence of all the rest of the company. I had nothing left for it but to fall fast asleep, which I did with all speed. "Come," said he, "resolve upon it, we will make a wedding at the next town: we will wake this pleasant companion who is fallen asleep, to be the brideman; and," giving the Quaker a clap on the knee, he concluded, "this sly saint, who, I'll warrant, understands what's what as well as you or I, widow, shall give the bride as father." The Quaker, who happened to be a man of smartness, answered, "Friend, I take it in good part that thou hast given me the authority of a father over this comely and virtuous child; and I must assure thee, that if I have the giving her, I shall not bestow her on thee. Thy mirth, friend, savoureth of folly; thou art a person of a light mind; thy drum is a type of thee — it soundeth because it is empty. Verily, it is not from thy fulness, but thy emptiness, that thou hast spoken this day. Friend, friend, we have hired this coach in partnership with thee, to carry us to the great city; we cannot go any other way. This worthy mother must hear thee if thou wilt needs utter thy follies; we cannot help it, friend, I say: if thou wilt, we must hear thee; but if thou wert a man of understanding, thou wouldst not take advantage of thy courageous countenance to abash us children of peace. — Thou art, thou sayest, a soldier; give quarter to us, who cannot resist thee. Why didst thou fleer at our friend, who feigned himself asleep? He said nothing; but how dost thou know what he containeth? If thou speakest improper things in the hearing of this virtuous young virgin, consider it as an outrage against a distressed person that cannot get from thee; to speak indiscreetly what we are obliged to hear, by being hasped up with thee in this public vehicle, is in some degree assaulting on the high road."

Here Ephraim paused, and the captain with a happy and uncommon impudence (which can be convicted and support itself at the same time) cries, "Faith, friend, I thank thee, I should have been a little impertinent if thou hadst not reprimanded me. Come, thou art, I see, a smoky old fellow, and I will be very orderly the ensuing part of my journey. I was going to give myself airs, but, ladies, I beg pardon."

The captain was so little out of humour, and our company was so far from being soured by this little ruffle, that Ephraim and he took a particular delight in being agreeable to each other for the future; and assumed their different provinces in the conduct of the company. Our reckoning, apartments, and accommodation fell under Ephraim; and the captain looked to all disputes on the road, as the good behaviour of our coachman, and the right we had of taking place, as going to London, of all vehicles coming from thence. The occurrences we met with were ordinary, and very little happened which could entertain by the relation of them: but when I considered the company we were in, I took it for no small good-fortune, that the whole journey was not spent in impertinences, which to one part of us might be an entertainment, to the other a suffering. What therefore Ephraim said when we were almost arrived at London, had to me an air not only of good understanding, but good breeding. Upon the young lady's expressing her satisfaction in the journey, and declaring how delightful it had been to her, Ephraim declared himself as follows: "There is no ordinary part of human life which expresseth so much a good mind, and a right inward man, as his behaviour upon meeting with strangers, especially such as may seem the most unsuitable companions to him: such a man when he falleth in the way with persons of simplicity and innocence, however knowing he may be in the ways of men, will not vaunt himself thereof, but will the rather hide his superiority to them, that he may not be painful unto them. My good friend," continued he, turning to the officer, "thee and I are to part by and by, and peradventure we may never meet again; but be advised by a plain man: modes and apparel are but trifles to the real man, therefore do not think such a man as thyself terrible for thy garb, nor such a one as me contemptible for mine. When two such as thee and I meet, with affections as we ought to have towards each other, thou shouldst rejoice to see my peaceable demeanour, and I should be glad to see thy strength and ability to protect me in it."

T.

SIR ROGER AND SIR ANDREW FREEPORT.

[STEELE.]

NO. 174. — WEDNESDAY, SEPTEMBER 19, 1711.

HÆC memini et victum frustra contendere Thyrsin.
— VIRG. ECL. vii. 69.

THE whole debate in mem'ry I retain,
When Thyrsis argued warmly, but in vain. — POPE.

THERE is scarce any thing more common than animosities between parties that cannot subsist but by their agreement: this was well represented in the sedition of the members of the human body in the old Roman fable.[1] It is often the case of lesser confederate states against a superior power, which are hardly held together, though their unanimity is necessary for their common safety; and this is always the case of the landed and trading interest of Great Britain: the trader is fed by the product of the land, and the landed man cannot be clothed but by the skill of the trader; and yet those interests are ever jarring.

We had last winter an instance of this at our club, in Sir Roger de Coverley and Sir Andrew Freeport, between whom there is generally a constant, though friendly opposition of opinions. It happened that one of the company, in an historical discourse, was observing,

[1] Livii, Hist. Dec. 1, Lib. ii. cap. ii.

that Carthaginian faith was a proverbial phrase to intimate breach of leagues. Sir Roger said it could hardly be otherwise: that the Carthaginians were the greatest traders in the world; and as gain is the chief end of such a people, they never pursue any other: the means to it are never regarded; they will, if it comes easily, get money honestly; but if not, they will not scruple to attain it by fraud, or cozenage: and indeed, what is the whole business of the trader's account, but to overreach him who trusts to his memory? But were that not so, what can there great and noble be expected from him whose attention is for ever fixed upon balancing his books, and watching over his expenses? And at best let frugality and parsimony be the virtues of the merchant, how much is his punctual dealing below a gentleman's charity to the poor, or hospitality among his neighbours?

Captain Sentry observed Sir Andrew very diligent in hearing Sir Roger, and had a mind to turn the discourse by taking notice in general, from the highest to the lowest parts of human society, there was a secret, though unjust, way among men, of indulging the seeds of ill-nature and envy, by comparing their own state of life to that of another, and grudging the approach of their neighbour to their own happiness; and on the other side he, who is the less at his ease, repines at the other, who, he thinks, has unjustly the advantage over him. Thus the civil and military lists look upon each other with much ill-nature; the soldier repines at the courtier's power, and the courtier rallies the soldier's honour; or, to come to lower instances, the private men in the horse and foot of an army, the carmen and coachmen in the city streets, mutually look upon each other with ill will, when they are in competition for quarters, or the way in their respective motions.

"It is very well, good captain," interrupted Sir Andrew: "you may attempt to turn the discourse if you think fit; but I must however have a word or two with Sir Roger, who, I see, thinks he has paid me off, and been very severe upon the merchant. I shall not," continued he, "at this time remind Sir Roger of the great and noble monuments of charity and public spirit, which have been erected by merchants since the reformation, but at present content myself with what he allows us, parsimony and frugality. If it were consistent with the quality of so ancient a baronet as Sir Roger, to keep an account, or measure things by the most infallible way, that of numbers, he would prefer our parsimony to his hospitality. If to drink so many hogsheads is to be hospitable, we do not contend for the fame of that virtue; but it would be worth while to consider, whether so many artificers at work ten days together by my appointment, or so many peasants made merry on Sir Roger's charge, are the men more obliged? I believe the families of the artificers will thank me more than the household of the peasants shall Sir Roger. Sir Roger gives to his men, but I place mine above the necessity or obligation of my bounty. I am in very little pain for the Roman proverb upon the Carthaginian traders; the Romans were their professed enemies: I am only sorry no Carthaginian histories have come to our hands: we might have been taught perhaps by them some proverbs against the Roman generosity, in fighting for, and bestowing other people's goods. But since Sir Roger has taken occasion, from an old proverb, to be out of humour with merchants, it should be no offence to offer one not quite so old, in their defence. When a man happens to break in Holland, they say of him that 'he has not kept true accounts.' This phrase, perhaps, among us, would appear a soft or humorous way of speaking, but with that exact nation it bears the highest reproach. For a man to be mistaken in the calculation of his expense, in his ability to answer future demands, or to be impertinently sanguine in putting his credit to too great adventure, are all instances of as much infamy, as with gayer nations to be failing in courage, or common honesty.

"Numbers are so much the measure of everything that is valuable, that it is not possible to demonstrate the success of any action, or the prudence of any undertaking, without them. I say this in answer to what Sir Roger is pleased to say, 'that little that is truly noble can be expected from one who is ever poring on his cash-book, or balancing his accounts.' When I have my returns from abroad, I can tell to a shilling, by the help of numbers, the profit or loss by my adventure; but I ought also to be able to shew that I had reason for making it, either from my own experience or that of other people, or from a reasonable presumption that my returns will be sufficient to answer my expense and hazard; and this is never to be done without the skill of numbers. For instance, if I am to trade to Turkey, I ought beforehand to know the demand of our manufactures there, as well as of their silks in England, and the customary prices that are given for both in each country. I ought to have a clear knowledge of these matters beforehand, that I may presume upon sufficient returns to answer the charge of the cargo I have fitted out, the freight and assurance out and home, the custom to the Queen, and the interest of my own money, and besides all these expenses a reasonable profit to myself. Now what is there of scandal in this skill? What has the merchant done, that he should be so little in the good graces of Sir Roger? He throws down no man's enclosures, and tramples upon no man's corn; he takes nothing from the industrious labourer; he pays the poor man for his work; he communicates his profit with mankind; by the preparation of his cargo, and the manufacture of his returns, he furnishes employment and subsistence to greater numbers than the richest nobleman; and even the nobleman is obliged to him for finding out foreign markets for the produce of his estate, and for making a great addition to his rents: and yet 'tis certain that none of all these things could be done by him without the exercise of his skill in numbers.

"This is the economy of the merchant, and the conduct of the gentleman must be the same, unless by scorning to be the steward, he resolves the steward shall be the gentleman. The gentleman, no more than the merchant, is able, without the help of numbers, to account for the success of any action, or the prudence of any adventure. If, for instance, the chase is his whole adventure, his only returns must be the stag's horns in the great hall, and the fox's nose upon the stable door. Without doubt Sir Roger knows the full value of these returns: and if beforehand he had computed the charges of the chase, a gentleman of his discretion would certainly have hanged up all his dogs: he would never have brought back so many fine horses to the kennel; he would never have gone so often, like a blast, over fields of corn. If such too had been the conduct of all his ancestors, he might truly have boasted at this day, that the antiquity of his family had never been sullied by a trade; a merchant had never been permitted with his whole estate to purchase a room for his picture in the gallery of the Coverleys, or to claim his descent from the maid of honour. But 'tis very happy for Sir Roger that the merchant paid so dear for his ambition. 'Tis the misfortune of many other gentlemen to turn out of the seats of their ancestors, to make way for such new masters as have been more exact in their accounts than themselves; and certainly he deserves the estate a great deal better who has got it by his industry, than he who has lost it by his negligence."

T.

THE SPECTATOR ON STREET CRIES.

[Addison.]

No. 251. — Tuesday, December. 18, 1711

. . . . . .Linguae centum sunt, oraque centum,
Ferrea vox . . . . *Virgil*

A hundred tongues, a hundred faces, and one clanging voice.

There is nothing which more astonishes a foreigner and frightens a country squire than the cries of London. My good friend Sir Roger often declares that he cannot get them out of his head or go to sleep for them the first week he is in Town. On the contrary, Will Honeycomb calls them the *Ramage de la Ville* and prefers them to the sounds of larks and nightingales, with all the music of the fields and woods. I have lately received a letter from some very odd fellow upon this subject, which I shall leave with my reader without saying anything further of it.

"*Sir*,

"I am a man out of business and would willingly turn my head to anything for an honest livelihood. I have invented several projects for raising several millions of money without burdening the subject, but I cannot get the Parliament to listen to me, who look upon me, forsooth, as a projector; so that despairing to enrich either myself or my country by this public-spiritedness, I would make some proposal to you relating to a design which I have very much at heart, and which may procure me a handsome subsistance, if you will be pleased to recommend it to the Cities of London and Westminster.

"The post I would aim at is to be Comptroller General of the London Cries, which are at present under no manner of rule or discipline. I think I am pretty well qualified for this place, as being a man of very strong lungs, of great insight into all the branches of our British trade and manufactures, and of a competent skill in music.

"The cries of London may be divided into vocal and instrumental. As for the latter, they are at present under a very great disorder. A freeman of London has the privilege of disturbing a whole street for an hour together with the twancking of a brass kettle or a frying-pan. The watchman's thump at midnight startles us in our beds as much as the breaking in of a thief. . . . . . I would therefore propose that no instrument of this nature should be made use of which I have not tuned and licensed after having carefully examined in what manner it may affect the ears of her Majesty's liege servants.

"Vocal cries are of a much larger extent, and indeed so full of incongruities and barbarisms that we appear a distracted city to foreigners, who do not comprehend the meaning of such enormous outcries. Milk is generally sold in a note above *Elah* and in sounds so exceedingly shrill that it often sets our teeth on edge. The chimney-sweeper is confined to no certain pitch; he sometimes utters himself in the deepest bass and sometimes in the sharpest treble; sometimes on the highest, and sometimes on the lowest note of the gamut. The same observation might be made on the retailers of small-coal, not to mention broken glass or brick dust. In these, therefore, and in the like cases, it should be my care to sweeten and mellow the voices of these itinerant tradesmen before they make their appearance in our streets; as also to accommodate their cries to their respective wares; and to take care in particular that those may not make the most noise who have the least to sell, which is very observable in the venders of card-matches, to whom I cannot but apply the old proverb of *Much Cry but little Wool.*

"Some of these last mentioned musicians are so very loud in the sale of these trifling manufactures that an honest splenetic gentleman of my acquaintance bargained with one of them never to come into the street where he lived; but what was the effect of this contract? Why the whole tribe of card-match-makers which frequented that quarter passed by his door the very next day in hopes of being bought off after the same manner.

"It is another great imperfection of our London cries that there is no just time nor measure observed in them. Our news should indeed be published in a very quick time, because it is a commodity that will not keep cold. It should not, however, be cried with the same precipitation as *Fire!* Yet this is generally the case: a bloody battle alarms the Town from one end to another in an instant. Every motion of the French is published in so great a hurry that one would think the enemy were at our gates. This likewise I would take upon me to regulate in such a manner that there should be some distinction made between the spreading of a victory, a march, or an incampment, a Dutch, a Portugal, or a Spanish mail. Nor must I omit under this head the excessive alarms with which several boisterous rustics infest our streets in turnip season, and which are more inexcusable because these are wares which are in no danger of cooling upon their hands.

"There are others who affect a very slow time, and are, in my opinion, much more tuneable than the former: the cooper in particular swells his last note in an hollow voice that is not without harmony; nor can I forbear being inspired with a most agreeable melancholy when I hear that sad and solemn air with which the public is often asked if they have any chairs to mend. Your own memory may suggest to you many other lamentable ditties of the same nature, in which the music is wonderfully languishing and melodious.

"I am always pleased with that particular time of the year which is proper for the pickling of dill and cucumbers; but, alas! this cry, like the song of the nightingales, is not heard above two months. It would therefore be worth while to consider whether the same air might not in some cases be adapted to other words.

"It might likewise deserve our most serious consideration how far in a well-regulated city these humorists are to be tolerated, who, not contented with the traditional cries of their forefathers, have invented particular songs and tunes of their own: such as was, not many years since, the pastry man, commonly called by the name of the Colly-Molly-Puff; and such as is at this day the vender of powder and washballs, who, if I am rightly informed, goes under the name of Powder-Watt.

"I must not here omit one particular absurdity which runs through this whole vociferous generation, and which renders their cries very often not incommodious but altogether useless to the public. I mean that idle accomplishment which they all of them aim at, of crying so as not to be understood. Whether or no they have learned this from several of our affected singers, I will not take upon me to say; but most certain it is that people know the wares they deal in rather by their tunes than by their words; insomuch that I have sometimes seen a country boy run out to buy apples of a bellows-mender and gingerbread from a grinder of knives and scissors. Nay, so strangely infatuated are some very eminent artists of this particular grace in a cry that none but their acquaintance are able to guess at their profession; for who else can know that *Work if I had it* should be the signification of a corn cutter!

"Furthermore, therefore, as persons of this rank are seldom men of genius or capacity, I think it would be very proper that some man of good sense and sound judgment should preside over these public cries, who should permit none to lift up their voices in our streets that have not tuneable throats and are not only able to overcome the noise of the crowd and the rattling of coaches, but also to vend their respective merchandises in apt phrases and in the most distinct and agreeable sounds. I do therefore humbly recommend myself as a person rightly qualified for this post; and if I shall meet with fitting encouragement, shall communicate some other projects which I have by me that may no less conduce to the emolument of the public.

"I am,

"Sir, etc.,

"Ralph Crotchett."

SIR ROGER IN LONDON. [ADDISON.]

NO. 269.—TUESDAY, JANUARY 8, 1711-12.

Ævo rarissima nostro
Simplicitas.—OVID. ARS AM. LIB. i. 241.

AND brings our old simplicity again.—DRYDEN.

I WAS this morning surprised with a great knocking at the door, when my landlady's daughter came up to me, and told me, that there was a man below desired to speak with me. Upon my asking her who it was, she told me it was a very grave elderly person, but that she did not know his name. I immediately went down to him, and found him to be the coachman of my worthy friend Sir Roger de Coverley. He told me that his master came to town last night, and would be glad to take a turn with me in Gray's-inn walks. As I was wondering in myself what had brought Sir Roger to town, not having lately received any letter from him, he told me that his master was come up to get a sight of prince Eugene, and that he desired I would immediately meet him.

I was not a little pleased with the curiosity of the old knight, though I did not much wonder at it, having heard him say more than once in private discourse, that he looked upon prince Eugenio (for so the knight always calls him) to be a greater man than Scanderbeg.

I was no sooner come into Gray's-inn walks, but I heard

my friend upon the terrace hemming twice or thrice to himself with great vigour, for he loves to clear his pipes in good air (to make use of his own phrase), and is not a little pleased with any one who takes notice of the strength which he still exerts in his morning hems.

I was touched with a secret joy at the sight of the good old man, who before he saw me was engaged in conversation with a beggar man that had asked alms of him. I could hear my friend chide him for not finding out some work; but at the same time saw him put his hand in his pocket and give him sixpence.

Our salutations were very hearty on both sides, consisting of many kind shakes of the hand, and several affectionate looks which we cast upon one another. After which the knight told me, my good friend his chaplain was very well, and much at my service, and that the Sunday before he had made a most incomparable sermon out of Dr. Barrow. "I have left," says he, "all my affairs in his hands, and being willing to lay an obligation upon him, have deposited with him thirty marks, to be distributed among his poor parishioners."

He then proceeded to acquaint me with the welfare of Will Wimble. Upon which he put his hand into his fob, and presented me in his name with a tobacco-stopper, telling me, that Will had been busy all the beginning of the winter in turning great quantities of them; and that he made a present of one to every gentleman in the country who has good principles, and smokes. He added, that poor Will was at present under great tribulation, for that Tom Touchy had taken the law of him for cutting some hazel sticks out of one of his hedges.

Among other pieces of news which the knight brought from his country-seat, he informed me that Moll White was dead; and that about a month after her death the wind was so very high, that it blew down the end of one of his barns. "But for my own part," says Sir Roger, "I do not think that the old woman had any hand in it."

He afterwards fell into an account of the diversions which had passed in his house during the holidays; for Sir Roger, after the laudable custom of his ancestors, always keeps open house at Christmas. I learned from him, that he had killed eight fat hogs for this season; that he had dealt about his chines very liberally amongst his neighbours: and that in particular he had sent a string of hog's puddings with a pack of cards to every poor family in the parish. "I have often thought," says Sir Roger, "it happens very well that Christmas should fall out in the middle of winter. It is the most dead and uncomfortable time of the year, when the poor people would suffer very much from their poverty and cold, if they had not good cheer, warm fires, and Christmas gambols to support them. I love to rejoice their poor hearts at this season, and to see the whole village merry in my great hall. I allow a double quantity of malt to my small beer, and set it a running for twelve days to every one that calls for it. I have always a piece of cold beef and a mince-pie upon the table, and am wonderfully pleased to see my tenants pass away a whole evening in playing their innocent tricks, and smutting one another. Our friend Will Wimble is as merry as any of them, and shews a thousand roguish tricks upon these occasions."

I was very much delighted with the reflexion of my

old friend, which carried so much goodness in it. He then launched out into the praise of the late act of parliament for securing the Church of England, and told me, with great satisfaction, that he believed it already began to take effect, for that a rigid dissenter, who chanced to dine at his house on Christmas day, had been observed to eat very plentifully of his plum-porridge.

After having despatched all our country matters, Sir Roger made several inquiries concerning the club, and particularly of his old antagonist Sir Andrew Freeport. He asked me with a kind of smile, whether Sir Andrew had not taken the advantage of his absence to vent among them some of his republican doctrines; but soon after, gathering up his countenance into a more than ordinary seriousness, "Tell me truly," says he, "don't you think Sir Andrew had a hand in the pope's procession?"—but without giving me time to answer him, "Well, well," says he, "I know you are a wary man, and do not care for talking of public matters."

The knight then asked me if I had seen prince Eugenio, and made me promise to get him a stand in some convenient place where he might have a full sight of that extraordinary man, whose presence does so much honour to the British nation. He dwelt very long on the praises of this great general, and I found that, since I was with him in the country, he had drawn many observations together out of his reading in Baker's Chronicle, and other authors, who always lie in his hall window, which very much redound to the honour of this prince.

Having passed away the greatest part of the morning in hearing the knight's reflexions, which were partly private and partly political, he asked me if I would smoke a pipe with him over a dish of coffee at Squire's? As I love the old man, I take delight in complying with everything that is agreeable to him, and accordingly waited on him to the coffee house, where his venerable aspect drew upon us the eyes of the whole room. He had no sooner seated himself at the upper end of the high table, but he called for a clean pipe, a paper of tobacco, a dish of coffee, a wax-candle, and the Supplement, with such an air of cheerfulness and good-humour, that all the boys in the coffee-room (who seemed to take pleasure in serving him) were at once employed on his several errands, insomuch that no body else could come at a dish of tea, till the knight had got all his conveniences about him.

L.

Westminster Abbey; Henry VII Chapel

WESTMINSTER ABBEY; EDWARD THE CONFESSOR'S CHAPEL

(*Publishers Photo Service.*)

SIR ROGER IN WESTMINSTER ABBEY. [ADDISON.]

NO. 329. — TUESDAY, MARCH 18, 1711–12.

IRE tamen restat, Numo quo devenit, et Ancus.
— HOR. EP. vi. Lib. I. 27.

IT yet remains to tread the drear descent,
Where good Pompelius, and great Ancus went.

MY friend Sir Roger de Coverley told me t'other night, that he had been reading my paper upon Westminster Abbey, in which, says he, there are a great many ingenious fancies. He told me at the same time, that he observed I had promised another paper upon the tombs, and that he should be glad to go and see them with me, not having visited them since he had read history. I could not imagine how this came into the knight's head, till I recollected that he had been very busy all last summer upon Baker's Chronicle, which he has quoted several times in his disputes with Sir Andrew Freeport since his last coming to town. Accordingly I promised to call upon him the next morning, that we might go together to the Abbey.

I found the knight under his butler's hands, who always shaves him. He was no sooner dressed than he called for a glass of the widow Trueby's water, which he told me he always drank before he went abroad. He recommended to me a dram of it at the same time, with so much heartiness, that I could not forbear drinking it. As soon as I had got it down, I found it very unpalatable; upon which the knight, observing that I had made several wry faces, told me that he knew I should not like it at first, but that it was the best thing in the world against the stone or gravel.

I could have wished indeed that he had acquainted me with the virtues of it sooner; but it was too late to complain, and I knew what he had done was out of good-will. Sir Roger told me further, that he looked upon it to be very good for a man whilst he stayed in town, to keep off infection, and that he got together a quantity of it upon the first news of the sickness being at Dantzick: when of a sudden turning short to one of his servants who stood behind him, he bid him call a hackney-coach, and take care it was an elderly man that drove it.

He then resumed the discourse upon Mrs. Trueby's water, telling me that the widow Trueby was one who did more good than all the doctors and apothecaries in the country; that she distilled every poppy that grew within five miles of her; that she distributed her water gratis among all sorts of people: to which the knight added, that she had a very great jointure, and that the whole country would fain have it a match between him and her; "and truly," says Sir Roger, "if I had not been engaged, perhaps I could not have done better."

His discourse was broken off by his man's telling him he had called a coach. Upon our going to it, after having cast his eye upon the wheels, he asked the coachman if his axle-tree was good; upon the fellow's telling him he would warrant it, the knight turned to me, told me he looked like an honest man, and went in without further ceremony.

We had not gone far, when Sir Roger popping out his head, called the coachman down from his box, and upon presenting himself at the window, asked him if he smoked: as I was considering what this would end in, he bid him stop by the way at any good tobacconist's, and take in a roll of their best Virginia. Nothing material happened in the remaining part of our journey, till we were set down at the west end of the Abbey.

As we went up the body of the church, the knight pointed at the trophies upon one of the new monuments, and cried out, "A brave man, I warrant him!" Passing afterwards by Sir Cloudesly Shovel, he flung his hand that way, and cried, "Sir Cloudesly Shovel, a very gallant man!" As we stood before Busby's tomb, the knight uttered himself again after the same manner. "Dr. Busby, a great man! he whipped my grandfather; a very great man! I should have gone to him myself, if I had not been a blockhead: a very great man!"

We were immediately conducted into the little chapel on the right hand. Sir Roger planting himself at our historian's elbow, was very attentive to everything he said, particularly to the account he gave us of the lord who had cut off the king of Morocco's head. Among several other figures, he was very well pleased to see the statesman Cecil upon his knees; and concluding them all to be great men, was conducted to the figure which represents that martyr to good housewifery, who died by the prick of a needle. Upon our interpreter's telling us that she was a maid of honour to Q. Elizabeth, the knight was very inquisitive into her name and family; and after having regarded her finger for some time, "I wonder," says he, "that Sir Richard Baker has said nothing of her in his Chronicle."

We were then conveyed to the two coronation chairs, where my old friend, after having heard that the stone underneath the most ancient of them, which was brought from Scotland, was called Jacob's pillar, set himself down in the chair; and looking like the figure of an old Gothic king, asked our interpreter, what authority they had to say, that Jacob had ever been in Scotland? The fellow, instead of returning him an answer, told him, that he hoped his honour would pay his forfeit. I could observe Sir Roger a little ruffled upon thus being trepanned; but our guide not insisting upon his demand, the knight soon recovered his good humour, and whispered in my ear, that if Will Wimble were with us and saw those two chairs, it would go hard but he would get a tobacco stopper out of one or t'other of them.

Sir Roger, in the next place, laid his hand upon Edward the Third's sword, and leaning upon the pommel of it, gave us the whole history of the Black Prince; concluding, that in Sir Richard Baker's opinion, Edward the Third was one of the greatest princes that ever sat upon the English throne.

We were then shewn Edward the Confessor's tomb; upon which Sir Roger acquainted us, that he was the first who touched for the evil: and afterwards Henry the Fourth's, upon which he shook his head, and told us there was fine reading in the casualties of that reign.

Our conductor then pointed to that monument where there is the figure of one of our English kings without an head; and upon giving us to know, that the head, which was of beaten silver, had been stolen away several years since; "Some Whig, I'll warrant you," says Sir Roger; "you ought to lock up your kings better; they will carry off the body too, if you don't take care."

The glorious names of Henry the Fifth and Queen Elizabeth gave the knight great opportunities of shining, and of doing justice to Sir Richard Baker, who, as our knight observed with some surprise, had a great many kings in him, whose monuments he had not seen in the Abbey.

For my own part, I could not but be pleased to see the knight shew such an honest passion for the glory of his country, and such a respectful gratitude to the memory of its princes.

I must not omit, that the benevolence of my good old friend, which flows out towards every one he converses with, made him very kind to our interpreter, whom he looked upon as an extraordinary man; for which reason he shook him by the hand at parting, telling him, that he should be very glad to see him at his lodgings in Norfolk Buildings, and talk over these matters with him more at leisure. L.

SIR ROGER AT THE PLAY. [ADDISON.]

NO. 335. — TUESDAY, MARCH 25, 1712.

RESPICERE exemplar vitæ morumque jubebo
Doctum imitatorem, et veras hinc ducere voces.
— HOR. ARS POET. 327.

KEEP Nature's great original in view,
And thence the living images pursue. — FRANCIS.

MY friend Sir Roger de Coverley, when we last met together at the club, told me that he had a great mind to see the new tragedy with me, assuring me at the same time, that he had not been at a play these twenty years. "The last I saw," said Sir Roger, "was *The Committee*, which I should not have gone to neither, had not I been told before-hand that it was a good church of England comedy." He then proceeded to inquire of me who this *Distressed Mother* was; and upon hearing that she was Hector's widow, he told me that her husband was a brave man, and that when he was a school-boy he had read his life at the end of the dictionary. My friend asked me, in the next place, if there would not be some danger in coming home late, in case the Mohocks should be abroad. "I assure you," says he, "I thought I had fallen into their hands last night; for I observed two or three lusty black men that followed me half way up Fleet-street, and mended their pace behind

THE DUKE'S PLAYHOUSE

Pulled down about the time of Addison and Steele. Many a famous play was produced here before King Charles II and King James II, the father of Queen Anne. (*From the theatre collection of Harvard College.*)

A THEATER TICKET DESIGNED BY HOGARTH

(*Boston Public Library.*)

me, in proportion as I put on to get away from them. You must know," continued the knight, with a smile, "I fancied they had a mind to *hunt* me; for I remember an honest gentleman in my neighbourhood, who was served such a trick in king Charles II's time, for which reason he has not ventured himself in town ever since. I might have shewn them very good sport, had this been their design; for as I am an old fox-hunter, I should have turned and dodged, and have played them a thousand tricks they had never seen in their lives before." Sir Roger added, that if these gentlemen had any such intention, they did not succeed very well in it; "for I threw them out," says he, "at the end of Norfolk-street, where I doubled the corner, and got shelter in my lodgings before they could imagine what was become of me. However," says the knight, "if Captain Sentry will make one with us to-morrow night, and if you will both of you call upon me about four o'clock, that we may be at the house before it is full, I will have my own coach in readiness to attend you, for John tells me he has got the fore-wheels mended."

The Captain, who did not fail to meet me there at the appointed hour, bid Sir Roger fear nothing, for that he had put on the same sword which he made use of at the battle of Steenkirk. Sir Roger's servants, and among the rest, my old friend the butler, had, I found, provided themselves with good oaken plants, to attend their master upon this occasion. When we had placed him in his coach, with myself at his left hand, the Captain before him, and his butler at the head of his footmen in the rear, we convoyed him in safety to the playhouse, where, having marched up the entry in good order, the Captain and I went in with him, and seated him betwixt us in the pit. As soon as the house was full, and the candles lighted, my old friend stood up and looked about him with that pleasure, which a mind seasoned with humanity naturally feels in itself, at the sight of a multitude of people who seem pleased with one another, and partake of the same common entertainment. I could not but fancy myself, as the old man stood up in the middle of the pit, that he made a very proper centre to a tragic audience. Upon the entering of Pyrrhus, the knight told me that he did not believe the king of France himself had a better strut. I was indeed very attentive to my old friend's remarks, because I looked upon them as a piece of natural criticism; and was well pleased to hear him, at the conclusion of almost every scene, telling me that he could not imagine how the play would end. One while he appeared much concerned for Andromache, and a little while after as much for Hermione; and was extremely puzzled to think what would become of Pyrrhus.

When Sir Roger saw Andromache's obstinate refusal to her lover's importunities, he whispered me in the ear, that he was sure she would never have him; to which he added, with a more than ordinary vehemence, "You can't imagine, Sir, what it is to have to do with a widow." Upon Pyrrhus his threatening afterwards to leave her, the knight shook his head, and muttered to himself, "Ay, do if you can." This part dwelt so much upon my friend's imagination, that at the close of the third act, as I was thinking of something else, he whispered me in my ear, "These widows, Sir, are the most perverse creatures in the world. But pray," says he, "you that are a critic, is this play according to your dramatic rules, as you call them? Should your people in tragedy always talk to be understood? Why, there is not a single sentence in this play that I do not know the meaning of."

The fourth act very unluckily began before I had time to give the old gentleman an answer: "Well," says the knight, sitting down with great satisfaction, "I suppose we are now to see Hector's ghost." He then renewed his attention, and from time to time fell a-praising the widow. He made, indeed, a little mistake as to one of her pages, whom at his first entering he took for Astyanax: but he quickly set himself right in that particular, though, at the same time, he owned he should have been very glad to have seen the little boy. "Who," says he, "must needs be a very fine child by the account that is given of him." Upon Hermione's going off with a menace to Pyrrhus, the audience gave a loud clap; to which Sir Roger added, "On my word, a notable young baggage!"

As there was a very remarkable silence and stillness in the audience during the whole action, it was natural for them to take the opportunity of the intervals between the acts, to express their opinion of the players, and of their respective parts. Sir Roger hearing a cluster of them praise Orestes, struck in with them, and told them that he thought his friend Pylades was a very sensible man; as they were afterwards applauding Pyrrhus, Sir Roger put in a second time, "And let me tell you," says he, "though he speak but little, I like the old fellow in whiskers as well as any of them." Captain Sentry, seeing two or three wags who sat near us, lean with an attentive ear towards Sir Roger, and fearing lest they should smoke the knight, plucked him by the elbow, and whispered something in his ear, that lasted till the opening of the fifth act. The knight was wonderfully attentive to the account which Orestes gives of Pyrrhus his death, and at the conclusion of it told me, it was such a bloody piece of work, that he was glad it was not done upon the stage. Seeing afterwards Orestes in his raving fit, he grew more than ordinary serious, and took occasion to moralise (in his way) upon an evil conscience, adding, that Orestes, in his madness, looked as if he saw something.

As we were the first that came into the house, so we were the last that went out of it; being resolved to have a clear passage for our old friend, whom we did not care to venture among the justling of the crowd. Sir Roger went out fully satisfied with his entertainment, and we guarded him to his lodging in the same manner that we brought him to the play-house; being highly pleased for my own part, not only with the performance of the excellent piece which had been presented, but with the satisfaction which it had given to the old man.

L.

SIR ROGER AND WILL HONEYCOMB.

[BUDGELL.]

NO. 359. — TUESDAY, APRIL 22, 1712.

TORVA leæna lupum sequitur, lupus ipse capellam;
Florentem cytisum sequitur lasciva capella. — VIRG. ECL. vi. 63

LIONS the wolves, and wolves the kids pursue,
The kids sweet thyme, — and still I follow you. — WARTON.

As we were at the club last night, I observed that my old friend Sir Roger, contrary to his usual custom, sat very silent, and instead of minding what was said by the company, was whistling to himself in a very thoughtful mood, and playing with a cork. I jogged Sir Andrew Freeport who sat between us; and as we were both observing him, we saw the knight shake his head, and heard him say to himself, "A foolish woman! I can't believe it." Sir Andrew gave him a gentle pat upon the shoulder, and offered to lay him a bottle of wine that he was thinking of the widow. My old friend started, and recovering out of his brown study, told Sir Andrew that once in his life he had been in the right. In short, after some little hesitation, Sir Roger told us in the fulness of his heart that he had just received a letter from his steward which acquainted him that his old rival and antagonist in the county, Sir David Dundrum, had been making a visit to the widow. "However," says Sir Roger, "I can never think that she'll have a man that's half a year older than I am, and a noted Republican into the bargain."

Will Honeycomb, who looks upon love as his particular province, interrupting our friend with a jaunty laugh, "I thought, knight," said he, "thou hadst lived long enough in the world, not to pin thy happiness upon one that is a woman and a widow. I think that without vanity I may pretend to know as much of the female world as any man in Great Britain, though the chief of my knowledge consists in this, that they are not to be known." Will immediately, with his usual fluency, rambled into an account of his own amours. "I am now," says he, "upon the verge of fifty" (though by the way we all knew he was turned of threescore). "You may easily guess," continued Will, "that I have not lived so long in the world without having had some thoughts of settling in it, as the phrase is. To tell you truly, I have several times tried my fortune that way, though I can't much boast of my success.

"I made my first addresses to a young lady in the country; but when I thought things were pretty well drawing to a conclusion, her father happening to hear that I had formerly boarded with a surgeon, the old put forbade me his house, and within a fortnight after married his daughter to a fox-hunter in the neighbourhood.

"I made my next applications to a widow, and attacked her so briskly, that I thought myself within a fortnight of her. As I waited upon her one morning, she told me that she intended to keep her ready-money and jointure in her own hand, and desired me to call upon her attorney in Lyon's-inn, who would adjust with me what it was proper for me to add to it. I was so rebuffed by this overture, that I never inquired either for her or her attorney afterwards.

"A few months after, I addressed myself to a young lady, who was an only daughter, and of a good family. I danced with her at several balls, squeezed her by the hand, said soft things to her, and, in short, made no doubt of her heart; and though my fortune was not equal to hers, I was in hopes that her fond father would not deny her the man she had fixed her affections upon. But as I went one day to the house in order to break the matter to him, I found the whole family in confusion, and heard to my unspeakable surprise, that Miss Jenny was that very morning run away with the butler.

"I then courted a second widow, and am at a loss to this day how I came to miss her, for she had often commended my person and behaviour. Her maid indeed told me one day, that her mistress said she never saw a gentleman with such a spindle pair of legs as Mr. Honeycomb.

"After this I laid siege to four heiresses successively, and being a handsome young dog in those days, quickly made a breach in their hearts; but I don't know how it came to pass, though I seldom failed of getting the daughter's consent, I could never in my life get the old people on my side.

"I could give you an account of a thousand other unsuccessful attempts, particularly of one which I made some years since upon an old woman, whom I had certainly borne away with flying colours, if her relations had not come pouring in to her assistance from all parts of

England; nay, I believe I should have got her at last, had not she been carried off by a hard frost."

As Will's transitions are extremely quick, he turned from Sir Roger, and, applying himself to me, told me there was a passage in the book I had considered last Saturday, which deserved to be writ in letters of gold; and taking out a pocket Milton read the following lines, which are part of one of Adam's speeches to Eve after the fall.

"Oh! why did our
Creator wise, that peopled highest heav'n
With spirits masculine, create at last
This novelty on earth, this fair defect
Of nature? and not fill the world at once
With men, as angels, without feminine?
Or find some other way to generate
Mankind? This mischief had not then befall'n,
And more that shall befall; innumerable
Disturbances on earth, through female snares,
And straight conjunction with this sex: for either
He shall never find out fit mate, but such
As some misfortune brings him, or mistake;
Or, whom he wishes most shall seldom gain
Through her perverseness; but shall see her gain'd
By a far worse; or if she love, withheld
By parents; or his happiest choice too late
Shall meet already link'd, and wedlock bound
To a fell adversary, his hate or shame:
Which infinite calamity shall cause
To human life, and household peace confound."

Sir Roger listened to this passage with great attention, and, desiring Mr. Honeycomb to fold down a leaf at the place, and lend him his book, the knight put it up in his pocket, and told us that he would read over these verses again before he went to bed. X.

SIR ROGER AT VAUXHALL. [ADDISON.]

NO. 383.—TUESDAY, MAY 20, 1712.

CRIMINIBUS debent hortos.—JUV. SAT. i. 75.
A BEAUTEOUS garden, but by vice maintain'd.

As I was sitting in my chamber, and thinking on a subject for my next *Spectator*, I heard two or three irregular bounces at my landlady's door, and upon the opening of it, a loud cheerful voice inquiring whether the philosopher was at home. The child who went to the door answered very innocently, that he did not lodge there. I immediately recollected that it was my good friend Sir Roger's voice; and that I had promised to go with him on the water to Spring-garden, in case it proved a good evening. The knight put me in mind of my promise from the bottom of the stair-case, but told me, that if I was speculating, he would stay below till I had done. Upon my coming down, I found all the children of the family got about my old friend, and my landlady herself, who is a notable prating gossip, engaged in a conference with him; being mightily pleased with his stroking her little boy on tne head, and bidding him to be a good child, and mind his book.

We were no sooner come to the Temple-stairs, but we were surrounded with a crowd of water-men, offering us their respective services. Sir Roger, after having looked about him very attentively, spied one with a wooden leg, and immediately gave him orders to get his boat ready. As we were walking towards it, "You must know," says Sir Roger, "I never make use of anybody to row me, that has not either lost a leg or an arm. I would rather bate him a few strokes of his oar than not employ an honest man that has been wounded in the Queen's service. If I was a lord or a bishop, and kept a barge, I would not put a fellow in my livery that had not a wooden leg."

My old friend, after having seated himself and trimmed the boat with his coachman, who, being a very sober man, always serves for ballast on these occasions, we made the best of our way for Vaux-hall. Sir Roger obliged the waterman to give us the history of his right leg, and hearing that he had left it at La Hogue, with many particulars which passed in that glorious action, the knight, in the triumph of his heart, made several reflexions on the greatness of the British nation; as, that one Englishman could beat three Frenchmen; that we could never be in danger of popery so long as we took care of our fleet; that the Thames was the noblest river in Europe; that London bridge was a greater piece of work than any of the seven wonders of the world; with many other honest prejudices which naturally cleave to the heart of a true Englishman.

After some short pause, the old knight turning about his head twice or thrice, to take a survey of this great metropolis, bid me observe how thick the city was set with churches, and that there was scarce a single steeple on this side Temple-bar. "A most heathenish sight!"

HOGARTH'S "SCENE FROM THE BEGGARS' OPERA".

The kneeling actress (Polly Peachum) is the celebrated Lavinia Fenton, the toast of the Town, and the spectator with the book is the Duke of Bolton, who fell in love and later eloped with her. (*Courtesy of the National Gallery.*)

The Orchestra at Vauxhall

says Sir Roger: "There is no religion at this end of the town. The fifty new churches will very much mend the prospect; but church-work is slow, church-work is slow."

I do not remember I have anywhere mentioned, in Sir Roger's character, his custom of saluting everybody that passes by him with a good-morrow or a good-night. This the old man does out of the overflowings of his humanity, though at the same time it renders him so popular among all his country neighbours, that it is thought to have gone a good way in making him once or twice knight of the shire. He cannot forbear this exercise of benevolence even in town, when he meets with any one in his morning or evening walk. It broke from him to several boats that passed by us on the water; but to the knight's great surprise, as he gave the good-night to two or three young fellows a little before our landing, one of them, instead of returning the civility, asked us, what queer old put we had in the boat, with a great deal of the like Thames-ribaldry. Sir Roger seemed a little shocked at first, but at length assuming a face of magistracy, told us, *That if he were a Middlesex justice, he would make such vagrants know that her Majesty's subjects were no more to be abused by water than by land.*

We were now arrived at Spring-garden, which is exquisitely pleasant at this time of the year. When I considered the fragrancy of the walks and bowers, with the choirs of birds that sung upon the trees, and the loose tribe of people that walked under their shades, I could not but look upon the place as a kind of Mahometan paradise. Sir Roger told me it put him in mind of a little coppice by his house in the country, which his chaplain used to call an aviary of nightingales. "You must understand," says the knight, "that there is nothing in the world that pleases a man in love so much as your nightingale. Ah, Mr. Spectator! the many moonlight nights that I have walked by myself, and thought on the widow by the music of the nightingale!" Here he fetched a deep sigh, and was falling into a fit of musing, when a mask, who came behind him, gave him a gentle tap upon the shoulder, and asked him if he would drink a bottle of mead with her? But the knight, being startled at so unexpected a familiarity, and displeased to be interrupted in his thoughts of the widow, told her, *She was a wanton baggage*, and bid her go about her business.

We concluded our walk with a glass of Burton ale, and a slice of hung beef. When we had done eating ourselves, the knight called a waiter to him, and bid him carry the remainder to the waterman that had but one leg. I perceived the fellow stared upon him at the oddness of the message, and was going to be saucy; upon which I ratified the knight's command with a peremptory look.

As we were going out of the garden, my old friend thinking himself obliged, as a member of the *quorum*, to animadvert upon the morals of the place, told the mistress of the house, who sat at the bar, that he should be a better customer to her garden, if there were more nightingales, and fewer improper persons. **I.**

THE DEATH OF SIR ROGER. [ADDISON.]

No. 517.—THURSDAY, OCTOBER 23, 1712.

HEU pietas! heu prisca fides!—VIRG. ÆN. vi. 878.
MIRROR of ancient faith!
Undaunted worth! Inviolable truth!—DRYDEN.

WE last night received a piece of ill news at our club, which very sensibly afflicted every one of us. I question not but my readers themselves will be troubled at the hearing of it. To keep them no longer in suspense, Sir Roger de Coverley is *dead*. He departed this life at his house in the country, after a few weeks' sickness. Sir Andrew Freeport has a letter from one of his correspondents in those parts, that informs him the old man caught a cold at the county sessions, as he was very warmly promoting an address of his own penning, in which he succeeded according to his wishes. But this particular comes from a Whig justice of peace, who was always Sir Roger's enemy and antagonist. I have letters both from the chaplain and Captain Sentry which mention nothing of it, but are filled with many particulars to the honour of the good old man. I have likewise a letter from the butler, who took so much care of me last summer when I was at the knight's house. As my friend the butler mentions, in the simplicity of his heart, several circumstances the others have passed over in silence, I shall give my reader a copy of his letter, without any alteration or diminution.

"HONOURED SIR,

"Knowing that you was my old master's good friend, I could not forbear sending you the melancholy news of his death, which has afflicted the whole country as well as his poor servants, who loved him, I may say, better than we did our lives. I am afraid he caught his death the last county sessions, where he would go to see justice done to a poor widow woman, and her fatherless children, that had been wronged by a neighbouring gentleman; for you know, sir, my good master was always the poor man's friend. Upon his coming home, the first complaint he made was, that he had lost his roast-beef stomach, not being able to touch a sirloin, which was served up according to custom; and you know he used to take great delight in it. From that time forward he grew worse and worse, but still kept a good heart to the last. Indeed we were once in great hope of his recovery, upon a kind message that was sent him from the widow lady whom he had made love to the forty last years of his life, but this only proved a lightning before death. He has bequeathed to this lady, as a token of his love, a great pearl necklace, and a couple of silver bracelets set with jewels, which belonged to my good old lady his mother: he has bequeathed the fine white gelding, that he used to ride a hunting upon, to his chaplain, because he thought he would be kind to him, and has left you all his books. He has, moreover, bequeathed to the chaplain a very pretty tenement with good lands about it. It being a very cold day when he made his will, he left for mourning, to every man in the parish, a great frize-coat, and to every woman a black riding-hood. It was a moving sight to see him take leave of his poor servants, commending us all for our fidelity, whilst we were not able to speak a word for weeping. As we most of us are grown grey-headed in our dear master's service, he has left us pensions and legacies, which we may live very comfortably upon the remaining part of our days. He has bequeathed a great deal more in charity, which is not yet come to my knowledge, and it is peremptorily said in the parish, that he has left money to build a steeple to the church; for he was heard to say some time ago that if he lived two years longer, Coverley church should have a steeple to it. The chaplain tells everybody that he made a very good end, and never speaks of him without tears. He was buried, according to his own directions, among the family of the Coverleys, on the left hand of his father Sir Arthur. The coffin was carried by six of his tenants, and the pall held up by six of the *quorum*: the whole parish followed the corpse with heavy hearts, and in their mourning suits, the men in frize, and the women in riding-hoods. Captain Sentry, my master's nephew, has taken possession of the hall-house, and the whole estate. When my old master saw him a little before his death, he shook him by the hand, and wished him joy of the estate which was falling to him, desiring him only to make a good use of it, and to pay the several legacies, and the gifts of charity which he told him he had left as quit-rents upon the estate. The Captain truly seems a courteous man, though he says but little. He makes much of those whom my master loved, and shews great kindness to the old house-dog, that you know my poor master was so fond of. It would have gone to your heart to have heard the moans the dumb creature made on the day of my master's death. He has never joyed himself since; no more has any of us. 'Twas the melancholiest day for the poor people that ever happened in Worcestershire. This is all from,

"Honoured Sir, your most sorrowful servant,

"EDWARD BISCUIT.

"P. S. My master desired, some weeks before he died, that a book which comes up to you by the carrier, should be given to Sir Andrew Freeport, in his name."

This letter, notwithstanding the poor butler's manner of writing it, gave us such an idea of our good old friend, that upon the reading of it there was not a dry eye in the club. Sir Andrew, opening the book, found it to be a collection of acts of parliament. There was in particular the Act of Uniformity, with some passages in it marked by Sir Roger's own hand. Sir Andrew found that they related to two or three points, which he had disputed with Sir Roger the last time he appeared at the club. Sir Andrew, who would have been merry at such an incident on another occasion, at the sight of the old man's hand-writing burst into tears, and put the book into his pocket. Captain Sentry informs me, that the knight has left rings and mourning for every one in the club.

O.

WILL HONEYCOMB'S MARRIAGE. [ADDISON.]

No. 530.—FRIDAY, NOVEMBER 7, 1712.

Sic visum Veneri; cui placet impares
Formas atque animos sub juga ahenea
Sævo mittere cum joco.—HOR. OD. i. 33, 10.

So Venus wills, whose power controls
The fond affections of our souls;
With sportive cruelty she binds
Unequal forms, unequal minds.

IT is very usual for those who have been severe upon marriage, in some part or other of their lives to enter into the fraternity which they have ridiculed, and to see their raillery return upon their own heads. I scarce ever knew a woman-hater that did not sooner or later pay for it. Marriage, which is a blessing to another man, falls upon such a one as a judgment. Mr. Congreve's *Old Bachelor* is set forth to us with much wit and humour, as an example of this kind. In short, those who have most distinguished themselves by railing at the sex in general, very often make an honourable amends, by choosing one of the most worthless persons of it for a companion and yoke-fellow. Hymen takes his revenge in kind, on those who turn his mysteries into ridicule.

My friend Will Honeycomb, who was so unmercifully witty upon the women in a couple of letters, which I lately communicated to the public, has given the ladies ample satisfaction by marrying a farmer's daughter; a piece of news which came to our club by the last post. The Templar is very positive that he has married a dairy-maid: but Will, in his letter to me on this occasion, sets the best face upon the matter that he can, and gives a more tolerable account of his spouse. I must confess I suspected something more than ordinary, when upon opening the letter I found that Will was fallen off from his former gaiety, having changed Dear Spec, which was his usual salute at the beginning of the letter, into *My worthy friend*, and subscribed himself at the latter end of it at full length William Honeycomb. In short, the gay, the loud, the vain Will Honeycomb, who had made love to every great fortune that has appeared in town for above thirty years together, and boasted of favours from ladies whom he had never seen, is at length wedded to a plain country girl.

His letter gives us the picture of a converted rake. The sober character of the husband is dashed with the man of the town, and enlivened with those little cant phrases which have made my friend Will often thought very pretty company. But let us hear what he says for himself.

"MY WORTHY FRIEND,

"I question not but you, and the rest of my acquaintance, wonder that I, who have lived in the smoke and gallantries of the town for thirty years together, should all on a sudden grow fond of a country life. Had not my dog of a steward ran away as he did without making up his accounts, I had still been immersed in sin and sea-coal. But since my late forced visit to my estate, I am so pleased with it, that I am resolved to live and die upon it. I am every day abroad among my acres, and can scarce forbear filling my letter with breezes, shades, flowers, meadows, and purling streams. The simplicity of manners which I have heard you so often speak of, and which appears here in perfection, charms me wonderfully. As an instance of it, I must acquaint you, and by your means the whole club, that I have lately married one of my tenants' daughters. She is born of honest parents, and though she has no portion, she has a great deal of virtue. The natural sweetness and innocence of her behaviour, the freshness of her complexion, the unaffected turn of her shape and person, shot me through and through every time I saw her, and did more execution upon me in grogram, than the greatest beauty in town or court had ever done in brocade. In short, she is such a one as promises me a good heir to my estate, and if by her means I cannot leave to my children what are falsely called the gifts of birth, high titles and alliances, I hope to convey to them the more real and valuable gifts of birth, strong bodies, and healthy constitutions. As for your fine women, I need not tell thee that I know them. I have had my share in their graces, but no more of that. It shall be my business hereafter to live the life of an honest man, and to act as becomes the master of a family. I question not but I shall draw upon me the raillery of the town, and be treated to the tune of *The Marriage-hater Match'd;* but I am prepared for it. I have been as witty upon others in my time. To tell thee truly, I saw such a tribe of fashionable young fluttering coxcombs shot up that I did not think my post of an *homme de ruelle* any longer tenable. I felt a certain stiffness in my limbs which entirely destroyed that jauntiness of air I was once master of. Besides, for I may now confess my age to thee, I have been eight and forty above these twelve years. Since my retirement into the country will make a vacancy in the club, I could wish you would fill up my place with my friend Tom Dapperwit. He has an infinite deal of fire, and knows the town. For my own part, as I have said before, I shall endeavour to live hereafter suitable to a man in my station, as a prudent head of a family, a good husband, a careful father (when it shall so happen) and as

"Your most sincere friend and humble servant,

"WILLIAM HONEYCOMB."

THE CLUB DISSOLVED [ADDISON.]

NO. 549. — SATURDAY, NOVEMBER 29, 1712.

QUAMVIS digressu veteris confusus amici,
Laudo tamen. — JUV. SAT. iii. 1

THOUGH grieved at the departure of my friend,
His purpose of retiring I commend.

I BELIEVE most people begin the world with a resolution to withdraw from it into a serious kind of solitude or retirement, when they have made themselves easy in it. Our unhappiness is, that we find out some excuse or other for deferring such our good resolutions till our intended retreat is cut off by death. But among all kinds of people there are none who are so hard to part with the world as those who are grown old in the heaping up of riches. Their minds are so warped with their constant attention to gain, that it is very difficult for them to give their souls another bent, and convert them towards those objects, which, though they are proper for every stage of life, are so more especially for the last. Horace describes an old usurer as so charmed with the pleasures of a country life, that, in order to make a purchase, he called in all his money; but what was the event of it? why, in a very few days after, he put it out again. I am engaged in this series of thought by a discourse which I had last week with my worthy friend Sir Andrew

Freeport, a man of so much natural eloquence, good sense, and probity of mind, that I always hear him with a particular pleasure. As we were sitting together, being the sole remaining members of our club, Sir Andrew gave me an account of the many busy scenes of life in which he had been engaged, and at the same time reckoned up to me abundance of those lucky hits which at another time he would have called pieces of good fortune; but in the temper of mind he was then, he termed them mercies, favours of Providence, and blessings upon an honest industry. "Now," says he, "you must know, my good friend, I am so used to consider myself as creditor and debtor, that I often state my accounts after the same manner with regard to heaven and my own soul. In this case, when I look upon the debtor side, I find such innumerable articles, that I want arithmetic to cast them up; but when I look upon the creditor side, I find little more than blank paper. Now, though I am very well satisfied that it is not in my power to balance accounts with my Maker, I am resolved however to turn all my future endeavours that way. You must not therefore be surprised, my friend, if you hear that I am betaking myself to a more thoughtful kind of life, and if I meet you no more in this place."

I could not but approve so good a resolution, notwithstanding the loss I shall suffer by it. Sir Andrew has since explained himself to me more at large in the following letter, which is just come to my hands.

"Good Mr. Spectator,

"Notwithstanding my friends at the club have always rallied me, when I have talked of retiring from business, and repeated to me one of my own sayings, *That a merchant has never enough till he has got a little more,* I can now inform you, that there is one in the world who thinks he has enough, and is determined to pass the remainder of his life in the enjoyment of what he has. You know me so well that I need not tell you, I mean, by the enjoyment of my possessions, the making of them useful to the public. As the greatest part of my estate has been hitherto of an unsteady and volatile nature, either tossed upon seas, or fluctuating in funds, it is now fixed and settled in substantial acres and tenements. I have removed it from the uncertainty of stocks, winds, and waves, and disposed of it in a considerable purchase. This will give me great opportunity of being charitable in my way, that is, in setting my poor neighbours to work, and giving them a comfortable subsistence out of their own industry. My gardens, my fish-ponds, my arable and pasture grounds, shall be my several hospitals, or rather workhouses, in which I propose to maintain a great many indigent persons, who are now starving in my neighbourhood. I have got a fine spread of improveable lands, and in my own thoughts am already ploughing up some of them, fencing others; planting woods, and draining marshes. In fine, as I have my share in the surface of this island, I am resolved to make it as beautiful a spot as any in her Majesty's dominions; at least there is not an inch of it which shall not be cultivated to the best advantage, and do its utmost for its owner. As in my mercantile employment I so disposed of my affairs, that from whatever corner of the compass the wind blew, it was bringing home one or other of my ships, I hope, as a husbandman, to contrive it so, that not a shower of rain, or a glimpse of sunshine, shall fall upon my estate, without bettering some part of it, and contributing to the products of the season. You know it has been hitherto my opinion of life, that it is thrown away when it is not some way useful to others. But when I am riding out by myself, in the fresh air on the open heath that lies by my house, I find several other thoughts growing up in me. I am now of opinion that a man of my age may find business enough on himself, by setting his mind in order, preparing it for another world, and reconciling it to the thoughts of death. I must therefore acquaint you, that besides those usual methods of charity, of which I have before spoken, I am at this very instant finding out a convenient place where I may build an alms-house, which I intend to endow very handsomely, for a dozen superannuated husbandmen. It will be a great pleasure to me to say my prayers twice a-day with men of my own years, who all of them, as well as myself, may have their thoughts taken up how they shall die, rather than how they shall live. I remember an excellent saying that I learned at school, *Finis coronat opus*, you know best whether it be in Virgil or in Horace; it is my business to apply it. If your affairs will permit you to take the country air with me sometimes, you shall find an apartment fitted up for you, and shall be every day entertained with beef or mutton of my own feeding; fish out of my own ponds; and fruit out of my own gardens. You shall have free egress and regress about my house, without having any questions asked you; and, in a word, such a hearty welcome as you may expect from

"Your most sincere friend,

"And humble servant,

"ANDREW FREEPORT."

Notes and Lesson Helps.

THE SPECTATOR'S ACCOUNT OF HIMSELF.

Motto. The writers and readers of the days of Queen Anne were especially fond of these captions from the classics. In reading these *Spectator* papers, pay careful attention to these quotations, which will often help you to gain quickly the author's purpose and his point of view.

Page 1, Line 3. black. Dark or brunette, as in Shakespeare's sonnets to the "dark lady."

2, 1 ff. With this description of an estate more than six hundred years old, compare the following from Oliver Wendell Holmes:

"We Americans are all cuckoos, — we make our homes in the nests of other birds. I have read somewhere that the lineal descendants of the man who carted off the body of William Rufus, with Walter Tyrrell's arrow sticking in it, have drawn a cart (not absolutely the same one, I suppose) in the New Forest from that day to this. I do not quite understand Mr. Ruskin's saying (if he said it) that he couldn't get along in a country where there were no castles, but I do think that we lose a great deal in living where there are so few permanent homes."

Give at least three reasons why Americans move more frequently from house to house than do the Europeans.

2, 25. parts. Mental attainments.

2, 27. In portraying the silence of the Spectator, Addison is drawing somewhat upon his own character.

3, 15. Addison is here poking fun at the half-century controversy concerning the size of the Great Pyramid.

6, 8. Little Britain. Locate this street on the map; in Addison's time it was the center of the book trade. In the *Sketch-Book* Irving presents a fascinating essay on Little Britain. By all means read it.

6, 13. Signature. In concluding the publication of the *Spectator*, Steele tells us that Addison had contributed "all the papers marked with a *C*, an *L*, an *I*, or an *O*, that is to say, all the papers which I have distinguished by any letter in the name of the Muse Clio." Steele used the letters *R* and *T*.

1. Point out three advantages the authors gained by thus creating and speaking through the Spectator rather than in appearing in their own persons.
2. Do you agree with the Spectator that we do not read a book with pleasure till we know something of the appearance of the writer? Do you think the Spectator really believes this, or is he here humorous?
3. Go through this first essay carefully, making a summary of the different qualities attributed to the Spectator. Watch to see if these are maintained consistently in the following essays.
4. With this picture of the Spectator compare "The Author's Account of Himself" in Irving's *Sketch-Book*. Which account is the more minute? What resemblances and what differences do you note? Which do you regard as the more interesting?
5. What are four words you have added to your vocabulary from reading this essay? Use them correctly in sentences.

THE SPECTATOR'S CLUB.

As you read, notice carefully each word here used. Frequently you can infer the meaning of the word from the context. If you are still in doubt, by all means go for help to your friend the dictionary.

7, 4. The Roger de Coverley dance resembled somewhat a Virginia reel.

7, 15. Soho Square. Locate on the map this district of London. In subsequent papers Sir Roger is represented as living in other and less fashionable quarters.

7, 19–20. Lord Rochester and Sir George Etheredge were two prodigal gallants of the time of Charles II, Etheredge still being remembered as a writer of plays. To be the companion of such fashionable wits as Rochester and Etheredge and to kick an insolent sharper such as Bully Dawson made the young Sir Roger notable socially.

8, 20. justice of the *quorum*. Special justice of the peace, who in the English counties presided over the quarter sessions, or quarterly meetings, of the court having authority in criminal cases.

8, 23. the game-act provided that "no one not having forty pounds per annum [income], or two hundred pounds' worth of goods or chattels might shoot game."

8, 25–26. Inner Temple. See the map and the Introduction.

8, 31. Aristotle. 9, 1. Longinus. The famous critics of literature in antiquity, and Demosthenes and Cicero, the Greek and the Roman orators, attracted him more than did Littleton and Coke, the great English legal authorities.

9, 25. Rose. A well-known tavern close to the Drury Lane Theater.

11, 2. How far promotion in the army was dependent upon other things than merit and service is strikingly shown by an advertisement appearing in the *Post Boy* about six months after this issue of the *Spectator:*

"This is to give Notice, That Whosoever has a mind to treat about the purchasing of Commissions in the Army, either in the old Regiments, or others, let them apply themselves to Mr. Pyne at his Coffee House under Scotland Yard Gate near Whitehall, and they will be further informed about it."

12, 1. humourists. Look up carefully in a large dictionary the origin and the different meanings of *humor* and *humorist.* Master these words, for they appear frequently in these papers.

12, 22. Duke of Monmouth. A handsome but unfortunate son of Charles II.

1. Which of the members of the Club are given especially significant names?
2. Why does Steele refrain from naming definitely two members of the Club?
3. Account for Addison and Steele's purpose in selecting each member.
4. What eighteenth-century American would have felt very much at home with Sir Andrew Freeport? Why?
5. Select three adjectives to characterize Captain Sentry. Why, do you fancy, are we told that he is related to Sir Roger?
6. Who is the most highly esteemed member of the Club?
7. Where could you find the modern counterpart of Will Honeycomb?
8. What little acts recorded in this paper are especially significant in revealing character?
9. Do you find any examples of satire in this paper?
10. Imitating Steele's language as nearly as you can, describe each member of the Club.
11. Using this essay as a pattern, describe an imaginary club in your school.

SIR ROGER ON MEN OF FINE PARTS.

14, 6. Wit. Another interesting word with a large number of meanings. Look it up carefully. What does it mean here?

14, 10. abandoned. Lawless, impure.

15, 7. Lincoln's-inn-fields. A square west of Lincoln's Inn, which in Addison's time was the resort of "wrestlers, bowlers, cripples, beggars, and rabble of all kinds."

16, 4. good starts. He couldn't carry along his good ideas.

16, 20. Sir Richard Blackmore. Author of long-winded and very dull poems, from the preface to one of which, *Prince Arthur*, Steele here quotes.

17, 13. What is here the exact meaning of *polite?*

1. Summarize briefly Sir Roger's conception of true wisdom.
2. For what class of English society was this paper especially intended?
3. Do you here find any statements running counter to our ordinarily accepted beliefs?
4. Can you give examples of wise men who were not good?
5. Define *modesty* and *integrity*.
6. Can you cite instances of practical joking which were in poor taste?
7. Write an editorial for your school paper on the chief ideas suggested by this essay.

THE SPECTATOR AT HIS CLUB.

20, 5–6. opera and puppet-show. The reference here is to the Spectator's comments on the newly introduced Italian opera and on the Punch and Judy shows in which Punch often talked vulgarly and insultingly. See especially Nos. 13 and 20 of the *Spectator*.

20, 27. Horace and Juvenal. Latin satirists; **Boileau.** A famous French critic.

23, 2. Roman Triumvirate. This story may be found in *Julius Cæsar*, IV, iii.

1. State in your own words the chief idea underlying this paper. Can you give any present-day illustrations of it?
2. Do most of us react as did the various members of the Club when criticism is directed against us?
3. What is particularly typical of the Templar's method of defense?
4. What member of the Club would probably be the first to lose his temper if the argument grew too heated?

5. Did the Spectator show good judgment when he turned a deaf ear to all remonstrances?

6. If you do not recall Æsop's fable of the Sun and the North Wind, look it up. Which of the two the better typifies the nature of Addison's satire?

7. Find a sentence which states very clearly the chief purposes served by the *Spectator*.

SIR ROGER AT HOME.

Throughout this series of papers Addison and Steele are repeatedly giving little touches of character delineation. Watch carefully for these, for in their entirety they present a personality fascinating in itself and of importance in the development of English fiction.

25, 24. when he is pleasant upon. When he has his joke upon.

27, 27. In the *Tatler* and *Spectator* we find frequent advertisements of newly published sermons, then a very popular form of literature. The clergymen here mentioned were all among the foremost preachers of the late seventeenth century.

1. Was Addison satirical in his commendation of the Chaplain's reading other men's sermons? What do you think of the idea?

2. Which of the Chaplain's qualifications do you think best fitted him for his position?

3. Are any new traits of Sir Roger here brought out?

4. What do you regard as the best example of humor in this paper?

5. If you were an artist wishing to illustrate this essay, what passages would you choose?

6. What have we been told concerning Sir Roger's age? Do his acts seem in keeping with such an age, or do you feel that they are characteristic of a somewhat older man?

THE COVERLEY HOUSEHOLD.

According to the law of those days, when a tenant wished to transfer his holding (usually a piece of land) to some one else, he had to pay the landlord a sum of money, called a "fine." This money, or "settlement" as it is here termed, Sir Roger frequently used to make more comfortable some aging servant. The knight is also represented as equally considerate of the young; for we are told that when the son of a servant went into apprenticeship for some trade, Sir Roger paid for him the necessary fee.

30, 9. stripped. Deprived of his livery.

1. What connection is there between the motto and the contents of this essay?
2. Explain the meaning, as here used, of each of the following: *family; economy; pleasant; husband; dress; manumission.* Some of these will require a careful use of the dictionary.
3. In writing this essay had Steele any purpose beyond entertainment? If so, how did he try to accomplish this?
4. What devices are used in American industries to secure and hold the hearty coöperation of the employees?
5. Do you agree, or do you disagree, with Sir Roger's convictions concerning the desirability of thus bestowing his cast-off clothing?
6. Show how Sir Roger's character influences the conditions in his home.
7. If you were master of Sir Roger's household, should you wish your servants to be like his, or should you wish them to be more reserved?
8. What incident in the last paragraph is especially significant in revealing Sir Roger's character?
9. Give a character sketch of Sir Roger from the point of view of one of his servants.

WILL WIMBLE.

For us who live in a world where the captains of industry are national heroes, it is difficult to realize the feelings of many of the English gentry that to go into trade was degrading and disgraceful. The lot of the younger son of these times, reared as a gentleman and seeing the estate inherited by his oldest brother, was truly unfortunate. If he did not choose to enter the church or the army or law or medicine, he not infrequently became a dependent, like Will Wimble.

35, 10. officious. What shade of meaning in this word common today is here missing?

35, 14. tulip-root. The mania for tulips, which during the seventeenth century had raged first and hardest in Holland, still affected the England of Queen Anne.

1. What are four common sporting terms used in this paper? What does each mean?
2. What different things does Will's letter reveal to you concerning its writer?

3. Try to discover whether in England the older and the younger sons still fare in matters of inheritance as they did in the times of Queen Anne.

4. What similarities do you find in all of Will's activities?

5. Do you place the blame for Will's irresponsibility upon his social status or upon the nature of the man himself?

6. Do you think Will would probably have succeeded as a merchant?

7. What member of the Club would most heartily disapprove of Will?

8. Have we any Will Wimbles in America?

9. Is the Spectator's attitude toward Will Wimble one of sympathy? of amusement? of pity? of contempt? of indignation? of friendly interest?

10. Write a paragraph in the style of the Spectator upon some class of present-day busy idlers.

THE COVERLEY PORTRAITS.

39, 2–3. yeoman of the guard. Under *Beefeater* in most of the larger dictionaries will be found a picture of one of these men in costume.

39, 11. Tiltyard. Near St. James's Park, where tournaments were held. See map.

39, 26. coffeehouse. Jennie Mann's Tiltyard Coffee-House, a resort for military men.

40, 12. What dish is the modern equivalent of *white pot?*

41, 30–31. knight of the shire. The representative of the shire, or county, in Parliament.

42, 11. What is here the exact meaning of *husbandman?*

42, 23–24. battle of Worcester. Fought by the Cavaliers and the Roundheads in 1651.

1. What instances can you cite from this essay revealing Sir Roger's wisdom, and what revealing his simplicity?

2. How does the Spectator here characterize Sir Roger's manner of talking? Can you find in this essay any especially good illustrations of this characterization?

3. Which of Sir Roger's ancestors best represented his ideas of a gentleman?

4. Which preceding *Spectator* deals with the class represented by the "soft gentleman"? What was Sir Roger's attitude toward him?

5. Why did the English squires value so highly their portrait galleries?

6. What can you tell of the changing fashions in our own time?

7. Point out several instances of humor in this essay. Try to select an adjective, or adjectives, for characterizing Addison's humor.

THE COVERLEY GHOST.

43, 9. Psalms. Addison was especially fond of the *Psalms*, some of which he versified, thus composing such popular hymns as those beginning, "The Lord my pastures shall prepare" (*Spectator*, No. 441) and "The spacious firmament on high" (*Spectator*, No. 465). Here the reference is to *Psalm* 147, 9: "He giveth to the beast his food, and to the young ravens which cry."

44, 24. Mr. Locke. Locke's famous *Essay on the Human Understanding*, which had appeared about twenty years previously, was one of Addison's favorite books.

46, 15. Lucretius. A Latin philosophic poet of the century before Christ.

1. What was the Spectator's purpose in writing this essay? Where does he definitely state his reason?

2. How does this paper differ in tone from the preceding and from the following essays?

3. Do most people still have something of this same dread of the dark?

4. Point out three especially well-constructed sentences, and defend your choice.

SUNDAY AT COVERLEY HALL.

The typical English rural church of Queen Anne's time was built in the shape of a cross. The clerk, whose position was usually below the chaplain's pulpit, led the congregation in the responsive reading and otherwise assisted in the services. These country churches were supported largely by tithes — that is, taxes levied on livestock and grain. Often these taxes were paid reluctantly or were even evaded by those whom the Spectator here calls "tithe stealers."

1. What name do most Americans give to the religious body here called Churchmen? What term is used in England to denote Protestants other than those belonging to the Church of England? What was the attitude of most of these country folk toward Roman Catholics?

2. Explain the meaning of four unusual church terms here employed.

3. What picture of Ichabod Crane is suggested by line 48?

4. To read Irving's essay on the country church in his *Sketch-Book* is the next best thing to visiting such a place. Compare Irving's essay with Addison's as to tone, manner of telling, characters delineated, etc.

5. What three special values does the Spectator find in the country Sunday?

6. In what various ways has Sir Roger contributed to the support of his church?

7. Was Sir Roger a particularly devout man? Support your answer by evidence from the essay.

8. Do you consider the respect paid Sir Roger due to his wealth or to his personality?

9. Give several instances of the knight's humor as shown in this paper. Are these in keeping with what we have learned of his character?

10. Point out at least three effective uses of contrast in this paper.

SIR ROGER IN LOVE.

If the *Spectator* had developed into a consistent plot the beginnings of a story given in such papers as this, we should have witnessed the birth of the modern novel. Probably in deference to his very considerable number of women readers Steele chose to introduce this story of the Widow.

As sheriff, Sir Roger had the privilege of appearing in full dress on state occasions. His office made him a man of importance at these meetings of the superior court (assizes), which were held twice a year. Like most of the country squires of the day Sir Roger was not much of a reader and had probably forgotten most of his schooling.

56, 1. What classical story helps us understand the meaning of "conquer the sphinx by posing her"?

56, 28. *Dum tacet hanc loquitur*, *Even when he is silent he is talking of her.* By the satirist Martial who was born in Spain and flourished about 100 A.D.

1. What are five unusual words which we must conquer if we would read this essay intelligently?

2. Is the picture of Sir Roger in love in keeping with the previous portrayal of his character? Defend your answer.

3. What is the source of the humor in Sir Roger's calling, "Make way for the defendant's witness"?

4. What is the best bit of humor in this essay?

5. Little description of the Widow's personal appearance is here given. What feature of the Widow does the knight admire most?

6. What sentence in this essay sheds the most light on the character of the Widow?

7. Do you suppose that the Widow really was such a fine scholar as Sir Roger thought her?

8. How does your conception of the character of the Widow differ from Sir Roger's?

9. Why is it usually more effective to tell a story in the first person as Sir Roger does here?

10. Do you find in this essay any verb form which would not be thought good grammar today?

SIR ROGER'S ECONOMY.

60, 1–12. If Laertes had paid his debt, he would have been spared the current land tax of four shillings on a pound; but in his pride he prefers to be classed as a man of larger income than his estate really is worth.

61, 18. great vulgar. The poems of Abraham Cowley (1618–1687) were still greatly esteemed in the days of the *Spectator*. The lines to which Steele here alludes are:

"Hence, ye profane! I hate you all
Both the great vulgar, and the small."

These lines begin a paraphrase by Cowley of an ode by Horace.

1. What are the exact meanings of *economy*, *dipped*, *libertine*, *corn*, *magnanimity?*

2. Give this essay another title which will bring out clearly its central idea.

3. How does the Spectator's purpose in writing this essay differ from his purpose in the preceding essay?

4. Express in your own words the difference between the types represented by Laertes and by Irus. Do we have any corresponding classes in the present-day American life? Should you say we have more people of the type of Laertes or of the type of Irus? Which class, on the whole, makes the better citizens?

5. Are people dwelling in the country usually more contented than those living in cities?

THE SPECTATOR ON EXERCISE.

63, 13. Look up in a large dictionary the different meanings of *engine*. What definition explains Pope's use of the word in describing a pair of scissors? Does that same meaning apply here?

64, 17. spleen. Ill humor. **64, 19. vapors.** Dejection, "the blues."

1. This essay is especially well constructed in its movement from one topic to the next. Show that this statement is true.
2. Just what is the Spectator recommending in this paper? From which author should you rather expect such a paper, Addison or Steele?
3. When may labor become exercise, and when may exercise become labor? What is the relation of the two in Mark Twain's story of the whitewashing of the fence in *Tom Sawyer?*
4. Does Addison here have in mind any special class of readers?
5. Should you call Sir Roger an industrious man?
6. Can you cite instances of men possessing strong minds joined to weak bodies?
7. Should you place as high a value on riding as a means of exercise as does the Spectator?
8. What organizations are putting into practice some of the ideas advanced in this essay?
9. Does the average American believe the doctrine given in the last paragraph? Does he habitually act in accord with such a belief?
10. Can you discover any strokes of satire in this essay?

SIR ROGER AS A HUNTER.

Most Americans fail to realize how large a part the sport of hunting on horseback played in the life of the English gentry in the days of Queen Anne and still plays in the life of today. Many an English squire then spent a large part of his days in the saddle, chasing the fox or the hare. He leaped hedges recklessly and often trampled the grain in the fields in a fashion which we should think highly unjust. Usually these gentry were accompanied by a troup of servants on foot, bearing poles to help them leap ditches and marshes.

68, 7. the Bastille. A prison in Paris, destroyed by a mob on July 14, 1789. Today the French celebrate July 14 very much as we observe July 4.

69, 19. staked himself. What similar fate befell a horse in *Silas Marner?*

69, 22. beagles. Small, swift hounds. **69, 23. stop-hounds** were slower and were trained to halt at a signal from the hunter, as did Sir Roger's dogs when the pole was thrown before them.

69, 25. "If you would have your kennel for sweetness of cry, then you must compound it of some large dogs that have deep, solemn mouths, and are swift in spending, which must, as it were, bear the base in the consort; then a double number of roaring, and loud ringing mouths, which must bear the counter [high] tenor; then some hollow, plain, sweet mouths, which must bear the mean or middle part; and so with these three parts of music, you shall make your cry perfect; and herein you shall observe that these hounds thus mixed, do run just and even together, and do not hang loose off one another, which is the vilest sight that may be." — *Country Contentments, or, The Husbandman's Recreations*, by Gervase Markham, 1675.

73, 7. Pascal. An eminent French philosopher (1623–1662).

74, 9. Mr. Dryden (1631–1700). John Dryden was the greatest English poet, critic, and dramatist during the years when the writers of the *Spectator* were young men.

1. Do the lives of the people you know best, confirm the truth of the statements made in the opening paragraph of this essay?
2. Could the first paragraph be omitted without material loss to the paper?
3. Does this essay contribute anything new to our understanding of Sir Roger? What characteristics already brought out are here emphasized?
4. Is the knight a "good sport" in our sense of the term? Support your answer by references to this paper.
5. Is the picture of Sir Roger here drawn by Budgell consistent with that presented by Addison and Steele?
6. How do Sir Roger's little weaknesses affect our attitude toward him?
7. What was the Spectator's real purpose in hunting? Cite the line in which he states this most clearly.
8. What do you regard as the most beneficial kind of exercise for a high school pupil? For an American business man?

MOLL WHITE.

Twenty years before Addison wrote this paper our own New England was executing its witches at Salem, and even as late as 1716 a Mrs. Hicks and her daughter were hanged in Huntington, England, for selling their souls to the devil and raising a storm. Whenever a poor, ignorant, old woman reached her dotage and began to mumble to herself, her equally ignorant neighbors marked her as a witch, whose dog or cat was the devil with whom she conversed, and whose broomstick carried her through the air. She was capable of all sorts of mischief, such as those described in this essay. Then the neighbors might test her by throwing her into a pond. If she sank, she was innocent; if she floated, she was a witch.

76, 17. Thomas Otway was a seventeenth-century dramatist of moderate ability.

1. Why is the motto an especially appropriate one?
2. What is the purpose of this paper — to reveal to us country superstitions, to teach a lesson, to show us another side of Sir Roger's character? Support your position.
3. Name five kinds of mischief of which the witches were accused.
4. Point out the similarities in the attitude of the neighbors toward Moll White and the attitude shown by his neighbors toward Silas Marner.
5. Does Sir Roger secretly fear the wrath of Moll White?
6. How is the knight's kindness of spirit exhibited in this essay?
7. What is the Spectator's attitude toward Moll White?
8. Have you ever known in real life a character of the type of Moll White? If so, tell about him or her.

A COVERLEY PASTORAL.

80, 16. this woman. The Widow.

1. In this paper does the knight contradict any statements he had made concerning the Widow in No. 113?
2. What has been Sir Roger's earlier experience with a confederate?
3. Why does Steele introduce the incident of the servant lovers?
4. Does Sir Roger feel resentment toward the Widow? Has he any right to feel it? Give in your own words his attitude toward the Widow.
5. If the Widow were alive today, what kind of a life do you picture her living?
6. Show how Sir Roger's whimsical nature is illustrated in the final paragraph.

COUNTRY MANNERS.

86, 19. Conversation. This word is here used as it was in No. 109 to mean social intercourse.

88, 19. clown. Countryman.

89, 16. Revolution. About a quarter of a century before.

89, 19–20. western circuit. "One of the eight judicial divisions of England and Wales." — HUDSON.

89, 23–24. a letter from him. Some member of the class should look this up in No. 129 and make a report.

89, 24. expect every post. See *Spectator*, No. 129.

1. Is the first paragraph as true today as it was in Addison's time? Support your answer.
2. Find the line in this essay which best expresses what good manners are.
3. In what respects do present ideas of good breeding agree with those of the Spectator's day, and in what do they differ?
4. What was the Spectator's reason for mentioning "those who had been polished in France"?
5. Do you think there is now as much difference between town and country manners as there was formerly? Give reasons for your answer.
6. Give examples of differences in dress and in speech in the various parts of our own country.
7. Which is the better, to be dressed out of fashion but comfortably, or to be dressed in fashion but uncomfortably?
8. Have you ever been where good manners were carried to an excess, making you uncomfortable?
9. Do you think that Addison cared much about the modes and fashions of the nation? Why did he write about them?
10. Write a paragraph discussing briefly the manners of the eighteenth century, basing your discussion entirely on this paper.

THE SPECTATOR ON INSTINCT.

90, 2. Addison is said to have been very fond of watching poultry.

90, 18. demonstrative. The natural history of animals demonstrates or proves the existence of a God.

92, 31. sceptical men. Unbelievers in the existence of the Deity.

1. Do you think that the Spectator chose this subject for some special purpose?
2. What relation has this paper to the entire series?
3. Name and illustrate at least three traits of the Spectator's character appearing in this paper.
4. Give three examples, not found in this essay, of animals

particularly suited to the lives they live. Explain how this is so.

SIR ROGER AT THE ASSIZES.

102, 4. yeoman. A small landholder of the social order just below the gentry.

102, 5. within the game-act. See note on **8, 23**; page 185.

102, 11. shoots flying. That is, he was too much of a sportsman to fire at a sitting bird.

102, 23. cast and been cast. To win and to lose lawsuits.

105, 3. Saracen's head. This was a favorite sign of these times. See Introduction, p. xiii.

1. What is the relation between the first paragraph and the rest of the essay?
2. Did Sir Roger speak with sincerity at the assizes, or was he trying to make a favorable impression on his hearers?
3. Was the knight's settlement of the argument between Will and Tom a matter of tact? of evasiveness? of humor?
4. Why was Sir Roger so admired by the country people?
5. Did the innkeeper realize why the knight wished the sign altered?
6. What somewhat similar incident concerning a sign is related in Irving's "Rip Van Winkle"?
7. How do you suppose Sir Roger received the Spectator's answer given at the close of the paper?
8. What different devices for portraying character are used in this paper?
9. Does the Spectator ever grow satirical in this paper?

A STORY OF EUDOXUS AND LEONTINE.

"Addison wrote to Mr. Wortley Montague, on the day of the publication of this paper, 'Being very well pleased with this day's *Spectator*, I cannot forbear sending you one of them, and desiring your opinion of the story in it. When you have a son, I shall be glad to be his Leontine, as my circumstances will probably be like his.'" — Gregory Smith.

107, 24. threw himself into a court. Court of a king.

107, 30. acquainted with all the sciences. One of the most marked features of the age was the enormous interest in matters of science. This interest found its most notable manifestation in the work of the Royal Society.

108, 3. Gazette. See the Introduction, p. xxvi.

1. What is the meaning of the following: *a farm of three hundred a year; Inns of Court?*

2. Would the son of Eudoxus have been as successful had he been reared by his own father?

3. What is the difference between a *parable* and an *allegory?* Is this paper an allegory or a parable?

4. What is the central idea which Addison is here trying to drive home? Can you give any proverb containing a somewhat similar idea?

THE SPECTATOR ON PARTY-SPIRIT.

When Addison wrote this essay, the political feuds which had given rise to three revolutions in England during the seventeenth century were again threatening to break into civil war. The Whigs blamed the Tories for their loose ways of living which had become prevalent after the Restoration of Charles II, while the Tories regarded the Whigs as the sons of the harsh and bigoted Puritans. The extreme Whigs declared the Tories were endangering the Church of England by favoring the restoration of the Roman Catholic Church, while the extreme Tories declared that the Whigs were endangering the government by attempting to restore the Commonwealth. The abuse of "You're a popish cur" was answered with "You're a republican dog." Swift declared that "even the cats and dogs are infected with Whig and Tory animosity." Repeatedly in the *Spectator* Addison attempted to moderate this heat of party spirit between the descendants of the Puritans and those of the Royalists.

114, 27. Plutarch. The great Greek moralist and greater biographer (49 A.D.?–120 A.D.?), discussed *How a Man May Receive Advantage and Profit from His Enemies*, a part of which Addison here paraphrases.

115, 5. that great rule. The Golden Rule.

115, 24. different mediums. Well illustrated by the appearance of a stick or pencil partly submerged in water.

116, 13. postulatums. Things taken for granted.

116, 24. Guelfes and Gibellines. During the twelfth to the fourteenth centuries the Guelphs supported the side of the popes, and the Ghibellines the side of the German emperors.

116, 25. League. An organization formed by the Duke of Guise in the sixteenth century to prevent the accession to the throne of France of Henry IV, who favored the reform religion.

1. Who were the Roundheads and the Cavaliers?

2. Where does Sir Roger's discourse here fail to be very logical?

3. Give instances from American history where the country was divided by furious party strife.

4. Is it necessary to have political parties in order to carry on successfully the government of a democratic nation?

5. How can our public minimize the evils of party spirit?

6. To what extent is Plutarch's statement true today? Put your answer into the form of a short talk, enumerating two or three points and giving a brief discussion of each.

7. Evaluate the solution of the problem of party spirit as the Spectator suggests it.

SIR ROGER AND POLITICS.

119, 22. Diodorus Siculus. A Sicilian Greek of the first century B.C., who wrote an *Historical Library*. Much of this is no more trustworthy than the story here given.

120, 12. Spirit of passion and prejudice. Addison had suffered from this party spirit he here attacks. Six months before this essay appeared Swift had written to Stella, "At night I called at the coffee house, where I had not been in a week, and talked coldly a while with Mr. Addison; all our friendship and dearness are off; we are civil acquaintance, talk words of course of when we shall meet, and that is all." *Journal to Stella*, January 14, 1710–1711.

1. Select three words here employed in a sense slightly different from that in which they are used today, and explain the difference.

2. Study carefully the declaration of intentions Addison here proposes. What does he mean to say under this seeming nonsense?

3. What is the point in introducing the account of the work of the ichneumon?

4. Which do you enjoy the more, these papers treating on more serious themes or those dealing with lighter topics?

5. Is it true that party spirit rages more fiercely in the country than in the city?

SIR ROGER AND THE GIPSIES.

124, 20. Cassandra. Daughter of Priam, king of Troy. She possessed the gift of prophesying truly, but she was never believed.

1. What is the meaning of each of the following: *exert the justice of the peace, line of life, perigrinations?*

2. Has the Spectator any purpose in this essay beyond affording entertainment?

3. Why did not Sir Roger exert the law upon the gipsies? Are laws ever disregarded today for the same reason?

4. Point out the contrast between the two parts of this essay. Does the knight maintain one attitude throughout toward the gipsies?

5. How do you think people of today regard fortune tellers?

6. Have the tactics of fortune tellers changed very much during these two hundred years?

7. Did the Spectator believe in what the gipsy told him? Did Sir Roger believe in what she told him?

8. Compare the knight in his attitude toward the gipsies with the idea you gained of him in some previous essays.

A SUMMONS TO LONDON.

129, 3. foil the scent. Mix the scent, so the dogs are confused.

129, 7. In Addison's day London and Westminster were separate cities.

"London, so the Guides aver,
Shared its glories with Westminster."—DOBSON.

129, 25. white witch. One that worked good, as opposed to a black witch.

129, 29. Jesuit. The Whigs taunted the Tories with being friendly to the Catholic order, the Jesuits, who were accused of plotting to restore to the throne the House of Stuart; the Tories were suspicious of the Whigs, who were then out of power.

131, 8–9. smelling to. Smelling of, or smelling.

131, 13. cock and bull stories. Extravagant, hoaxing stories.

131, 19. commonwealth's man. The equivalent of calling a man a republican. As already noted, one of the taunts of the Tories was that the Whigs wished to reëstablish the Commonwealth of Cromwell's time. Which political party did Sir Andrew champion?

1. In what ways is this essay an excellent transition from country to city life?

2. Why is the first paragraph a very suitable introduction to this essay?

3. Why would not the Spectator fit well into country life?

4. Where does one feel freer from the public eye — in the country or in the city?

5. What different purposes are here served by Will Honeycomb's letter?

6. Is there anything especially significant about the close of the letter?

THE JOURNEY TO LONDON.

" The roads were bad almost everywhere, and no one traveled more than they could help. The coaches were heavy and strong to stand the fearful wear and tear; but, to the passengers, a journey was simply the time spent in torture. Even in London the stones jolted terribly." — Ashton's *Social England in the Reign of Queen Anne*, II, 168. Often the roads were so wretched that one vehicle had to pull out at the side while the other passed along the center. A fascinating picture of travel on the English roads at Christmas time is given in Irving's essay on the " Stage Coach " in the *Sketch-Book*.

132, 10. recruiting. The long and bloody wars with France had drained the country of able-bodied men, and recruiting officers often resorted to sharp practices to re-man the army and navy.

1. Explain the following: *he dealt much in intelligence, who happened to be a man of smartness*, and *a smoky old fellow*.

2. What are three unusual words you discover in this essay, and what does each mean?

3. Mention all the points brought out in this essay concerning travel in England at that time.

4. The quotation at the top of this paper is illustrated in all its parts by incidents of the journey. Point out these illustrations.

5. Is the chamberlain's description of the Spectator a true characterization?

6. How far does the Spectator's attitude toward the Captain coincide with that of the Quaker? Is the Spectator preaching to his readers through Ephriam?

7. Write a paragraph explaining just what Ephriam meant in his parting speech to the officer.

SIR ROGER AND SIR ANDREW FREEPORT.

138, 14. Distinguish between *parsimony* and *frugality*.

139, 27. Look up this story in the first scene of Shakespeare's *Coriolanus*.

140, 2 ff. " The influence of the industrial classes had for a long time been steadily increasing, with the accumulation of industrial wealth. . . . It was noticed, as a remarkable sign of the democratic spirit that followed the Commonwealth, that country gentlemen in England had begun to bind their sons as apprentices to merchants, and also, about the same time, the desire to obtain large portions in marriage led to alliances between the aristocracy and the merchants." — Lecky's *History of England in the Eighteenth Century*, Vol. I, Chap. II.

140, 7. kept true accounts. Many words thus connected with trade have significant histories. What, for example, is the origin of *bankrupt?*

141, 6–7. the custom to the Queen. Tariff duty.

141, 11–12. He . . . tramples upon no man's corn. "Hunting in summer would be a grievous sin against the sporting laws now in force; but from the time of Elizabeth to George III, standing corn — the mere bread of the people — was not allowed to interfere with the squierarchy in its devotion to the chase. In the ripening and harvest months, however hot the weather, sportsmen were permitted to gallop down the grain as ruthlessly as the cavalry of an invading enemy. The farmers complained piteously of the losses they suffered, but it was not until the farmer's friend, George III, came to power, that the abuse was abolished." — WILLS.

141, 20. rents. Income.

What words with an unusual meaning which you have already learned reappear in this essay?

141, 28. the merchant. To what incident recorded in No. 109 does Sir Andrew here refer?

1. Why does the Spectator return time after time to this serious and vexing question of party strife?

2. What sentence best expresses the difference between Sir Roger's and Sir Andrew's views of helping people? Which of these two has, in your opinion, the better method of dealing with men?

3. Can a merchant be a gentleman as Sir Roger interprets that type?

4. Does Steele's own sympathy with the Whigs here become too apparent? Is it significant that Steele rather than Addison wrote this essay?

5. Do we have differences between similar factions today, such as then existed between traders and the landed people?

6. In what affairs mentioned by Sir Andrew does our consular service help our merchants?

7. Why was Captain Sentry's speech here quite in keeping with his character? (See *Spectator*, No. 2.)

ON STREET CRIES.

143, 6. Ramage de la Ville. The warbling of town birds.

143, 18. Projector. Possibly Addison is here laughing good-naturedly at Dick Steele's projects — his many "get-rich-quick" schemes.

144, 14. the liberties. The territory in which certain privileges and immunities were enjoyed.

144, 27. elah. The highest note on the musical scale.

146, 26. Colly-Molly-Puff. "This little man was but just able to support the basket of pastry which he carried on his head, and sang in a very peculiar tone the cant words which passed into his name, Colly-Molly-Puff." — FERGUSON.

1. Is this picture in keeping with the general purpose of the *Spectator?*

2. Notice carefully the street cries familiar to you. Are any of the criticisms here offered applicable to those cries you know? For example, do newsboys cry their papers clearly? Are there any hawkers who appear on your streets at certain seasons only?

3. What is amusing about Ralph Crotchett's opinion of his invention?

SIR ROGER IN LONDON.

148, 10. Gray's-inn walks. See Introduction, p. x.

148, 18. Prince Eugenio. A famous general of the Austrian army coöperating with the English against the French. In January, 1712, he came to London to try to induce the English to restore to power his fellow general, the Duke of Marlborough; but this he failed to accomplish.

148, 19. Scanderbeg. An Albanian general of the fifteenth century, celebrated in the wars with the Turks. Some student should report on Longfellow's "Spanish Jew's Tale" in *Tales of a Wayside Inn.*

149, 24. tobacco-stopper. A small wooden plug for pressing tobacco into a pipe.

149, 28. good principles. Belonging to which political party?

150, 28. smutting one another. By being induced to make signs on their faces while holding a saucer blackened on the under surface. This is an old English country trick. Cf. Goldsmith's

"The swain mistrustless of his smutted face."

151, 3. securing the Church of England. The Occasional Conformity Act excluded from office the moderate dissenters who had formerly qualified by occasionally receiving the sacrament at an Anglican church.

151, 16. pope's procession. The anniversary of the accession of Elizabeth (November 17, 1711) was made the occasion of a great and riotous political disturbance. Swift in his *Journal to Stella* says:

"This is Queen Elizabeth's birthday, usually kept in this town by apprentices, etc.: but the Whigs designed a mighty procession by midnight, and had laid out a thousand pounds to dress up the Pope, Devil, Cardinals — etc., and to carry them with torches about and burn them. . . . But they were seized last night by order of the Secretary."

151, 27. Baker's Chronicle. A confused and unreliable account of English history from the Norman Conquest to the death of James I in 1625.

152, 2. Squire's. Squire's Coffee-House, near Gray's Inn, was a favorite haunt of lawyers and law students.

1. What is the Spectator's real purpose in bringing Sir Roger to town?
2. Give instances in which the arrival of a famous person has produced a stir in our own cities.
3. Give five bits of gossip which Sir Roger brings to the Spectator.
4. What is gained by having the knight thus inform us concerning the welfare of these country characters?
5. With the knight's description of the Christmas festivities compare Irving's Christmas series in the *Sketch-Book*.
6. What do you think of the wisdom of Sir Roger's method of distributing cheer to the needy?
7. What characteristics of Sir Roger make the boys in the coffee-house eager to wait on him?
8. What humorous characteristics of Sir Roger are brought out in this paper?
9. In several previous essays we have had examples of the characteristics brought out in the last paragraph. Name at least two of these.
10. This essay contains many well-constructed sentences. Point out several of these and defend your choice.

SIR ROGER IN WESTMINSTER ABBEY.

Addison was especially fond of this great national shrine in which his remains were destined to rest. In *Spectator* No. 26 he has written an interesting meditation on Westminster Abbey.

This may profitably be compared with Irving's treatment of the same subject in the *Sketch-Book*. Review what has been said in the Introduction of this volume, p. xx.

153, 17. widow Trueby's water. A mixture composed largely of distilled spirits.

154, 13–14. sickness of Dantzick. The plague from which Danzig had suffered grievously in 1709.

154, 27. engaged. Interested. Sir Roger and the Widow were never engaged in our sense of the term.

155, 16. Sir Cloudesley Shovel. A renowned English admiral (1650–1707). See the account of his monument in *Spectator* No. 26.

155, 17. Busby. For more than fifty years headmaster of Westminster School. He died in 1695.

155, 23–24. our historian. Our guide; later called "our interpreter."

155, 28. Cecil. William Cecil, Lord Burleigh, was lord high treasurer under Queen Elizabeth. He erected in Westminster Abbey a very gorgeous monument to the memory of his wife and daughter.

155, 30–31. The martyr who died by the prick of a needle. Elizabeth Russell was erroneously said to have died thus.

156, 29. touched for the evil. As a scrofulous child Samuel Johnson was among the last ever touched for the evil by an English sovereign (Queen Anne). Anne's successor, George I, discontinued the practice. See *Macbeth*, IV, iii, 146 ff.

1. Was this paper written simply to amuse its readers, or was it intended to convey some message to them?

2. Do we have any shrine in America corresponding to Westminster?

3. In what would you be most interested if you visited Westminster Abbey?

4. What characteristics of an old man are displayed by Sir Roger?

5. What is significant in his repeated allusions to *Baker's Chronicle ?*

6. Describe the Spectator's attitude here shown toward Sir Roger.

7. What does the knight's momentary irritation over the forfeit claimed by the guide indicate to us?

8. What are some of the devices used by Addison to produce upon the reader the impressions made upon him by the sights and associations in Westminster Abbey?

SIR ROGER AT THE PLAY.

158, 5–6. The Committee. By Sir Henry Howard, Dryden's brother-in-law. The play delighted the Tories by its satire on the Dissenters, who were Whigs. See Pepys's *Diary*, June 12, 1663.

158, 9. This *Distressed Mother*. By Ambrose Philips. It is here brought very skillfully to the public notice by his friend Addison. The plot runs thus:

After the fall of Troy, Pyrrhus, son of Achilles, who had slain Hector, proposes to Andromache, Hector's widow, that if she will wed him, he will make her son Astyanax the king of Troy; if she refuses, he will give Astyanax to the massacring Greeks. When Hermione, betrothed to Pyrrhus, learns that Andromache has consented, she induces her brother Orestes to rouse the Greeks, who kill Pyrrhus. Hermione commits suicide; Orestes is tormented by the Furies; and thus the "distressed mother," Andromache, is rescued.

158, 15. Mohawks. See Introduction, p. xxv. "Young Davenant was telling us at court how he was set upon by the Mohocks, and how they ran his chair through with a sword. It is not safe being in the streets at night for them. The Bishop of Salisbury's son is said to be of the gang. They are all Whigs; and a great lady sent to me, to speak to her father and to the Lord-Treasurer, to have a care of them, and to be careful likewise of myself; for she hears they have malicious intentions against the ministers and their friends." — "Here is the Devil and all to do with these Mohocks. Grub Street papers about them fly like lightning, and a list printed of nearly 80 put into several prisons, and all a lie; and I begin almost to think there is no truth, or very little in the whole story." — Swift, *Journal to Stella*, March, 1712.

159, 18. about four o'clock. Plays began at five or slightly after.

159, 25. the battle of Steenkirk. In this battle the French defeated the English and the Dutch, 1692.

159, 27. good oaken plants. Stout oak cudgels.

160, 3. pit. See the Introduction, p. xxiv.

161, 28. Pylades. Close friend of Orestes; the "old fellow in whiskers" was Phœnix, counselor to Pyrrhus.

162, 4. smoke. Make fun of.

1. Can you find any eighteenth-century slang in this essay?
2. Do you think *The Distressed Mother* was an especially good play?

3. What conditions made it easy for the Mohocks to prey upon pedestrians?

4. What do you consider the best example of humor in this paper? Does Addison ever become satirical here?

5. Which was the more interesting to the Spectator, Sir Roger or the play? Why?

6. Was Sir Roger's behavior at the theater in keeping with his conduct at church? At the assizes?

7. Go with Sir Roger to one of our modern movies, and record the comments he makes. Be sure that these remarks are quite in keeping with his character.

8. Imagine that last night you went to a play in Queen Anne's time. Prepare to tell the story of your evening's entertainment.

SIR ROGER AND WILL HONEYCOMB.

163, 10. to lay. To bet.

164, 23. put (pŭt). A slang term, equivalent to our "hayseed."

166, 5. the book I had considered. At that time Addison was devoting the Saturday *Spectators* to a series of criticisms of *Paradise Lost.* The passage here quoted from that poem is Book X, 888–908. What are three other words in this essay which require explanation, and what does each mean?

1. Give six traits of human nature depicted in this essay.

2. Find a clause which very cleverly and humorously shows Will Honeycomb's vanity.

3. Do you think Will Honeycomb told the truth in his account of his love affairs?

4. What is the real reason why he had not married?

5. Compare your attitude toward Will Honeycomb with your attitude toward some other member of the Club.

6. Explain Sir Roger's interest in the quotation from Milton. What do you think would have been Sir Roger's real feeling if the Widow had suddenly accepted his proposal of marriage? Support your answer.

SIR ROGER AT VAUXHALL.

Vauxhall, or Spring Garden, was a pleasant resort up the Thames, which was reached easily and cheaply by boat. The shady walks, the attractive supper tables, the music, the thousands of lamps with their colored glass, and the gay crowds were among the attractions. The place attained the height of its popularity in the mid-eighteenth century and appears frequently in the novels and the letters of the times.

167, 19. Temple-stairs. A stone landing leading from the Thames to the Temple grounds.

168, 16. La Hogue. A naval battle, 1692, in which the English and the Dutch defeated the French.

168, 31. this side of Temple-bar. Temple Bar marked the division between the city of London and Westminster. Sir Roger means that, while the City was well supplied with churches, Westminster was notably lacking. The knight here approves heartily of the act of Parliament, passed in 1710, providing fifty new churches for the City and its rapidly growing suburbs.

What have we learned was the meaning of "knight of the shire"?

169, 29–30. Mahometan paradise. The heaven described in the Koran was a garden abounding in everything gratifying to the senses.

Use in sentences the words *coppice* and *aviary*.

1. Can you invent a better title for this paper than this customary one?
2. In all their journeys together what is the attitude the Spectator repeatedly manifests toward Sir Roger?
3. Point out a sentence showing the Spectator in a somewhat different light from that in which we have seen him before.
4. Compare the knight's choice of a boatman with his choice of a coachman in No. 335.
5. What remarks here show Sir Roger's strong English prejudices?
6. What are some indications of Sir Roger's increasing age?

THE DEATH OF SIR ROGER.

171, 14. Captain Sentry. How was his relation with Sir Roger brought out in No. 2 of the *Spectator?*

172, 26. tenement. What reference in No. 107 prepares for this?

173, 1. peremptorily. Assuredly.

173, 17. quitrents. "Rents reserved in grants of land by payment of which the tenant is quit from other service, but, in this case, charges upon the estate." — DEIGHTON.

174, 2. Act of Uniformity. "Under which all ministers of the churches of England and Wales should accept the Book of Common Prayer and read morning and evening prayers from it."

More than two thousand ministers gave up their positions rather than do this.

174, 10. rings and mourning. "Beside the rings, hatbands, scarves, and gloves, there was another tax; for Evelyn, noting Pepys's death and burial, says, 'Mr. Pepys has been for 40 years so much my particular friend that Mr. Jackson sent me *compleat* mourning, desiring me to be one to hold up the pall at his magnificent obsequies, but my indisposition hindered me from doing him this last office.'" — Ashton, *Social Life in the Reign of Queen Anne*, Vol. I, p. 52.

1. How do you suppose the readers of the *Spectator* received this paper?
2. Do you know of any newspaper characters today whose "death" would produce a similar effect?
3. What is gained by thus presenting the account of the death of Sir Roger in the form of a letter from the butler? Show how the style and content of the letter are quite in keeping with the character of the butler.
4. What traits of Sir Roger do you find carried out even to the end?
5. What do you imagine were the Widow's feelings at the death of Sir Roger?
6. Write a present-day account of the death of Sir Roger, such as might appear in a *good* small-town newspaper.

WILL HONEYCOMB'S MARRIAGE.

175, 8. Congreve's Old Bachelor. This play, which was one of Addison's favorites, was produced by his friend Congreve in 1693. At that time Dryden had praised it as the best first play he had ever known.

175, 16. a couple of letters. See the *Spectator*, Nos. 499, 511.

177, 25–26. homme de ruelle. Society man.

1. What sentence summarizes well the character of Will Honeycomb as he has appeared in previous essays?
2. Comment on the style of Will Honeycomb's letter. Do you here discover any clever phrases?

THE CLUB DISSOLVED.

A week after the appearance of this number Addison and Steele discontinued their publication of the *Spectator*. One by one the members of the Club had been disposed of. Captain

Sentry had left London to manage the country estate which he had inherited from Sir Roger. The Templar relinquished literature for the serious study of the law, and after a lingering illness the Clergyman had died. Here we catch a final view of Sir Andrew.

180, 14. fish-ponds. In those days before the refrigeration of meats, much fish was consumed; the pond was a common feature of a country gentleman's estate.

181, 8–9. Finis coronat opus. Meaning?

181, 9. Virgil and Horace. Examine the mottoes prefacing these different papers to learn who were the Spectator's favorite classical authors.

1. What are some distinctly eighteenth-century phrases appearing in this essay?
2. How does the style of Sir Andrew's letter differ from that of Will Honeycomb's?
3. Show how Sir Andrew proposes to carry out his idea of the right relation of capital and labor as suggested in No. 137.
4. What sentence here gives the best insight into Sir Andrew's character?

QUESTIONS FOR FURTHER STUDY AND FOR REVIEW.

1. Describe the Club as to (1) its organization and membership, (2) its purpose, and (3) the final dispersing of its members.
2. Describe one of Sir Roger's ancestors.
3. Give a brief sketch of the life of Sir Roger.
4. If you were invited to visit for a week at Sir Roger's, how should you plan to spend your time?
5. What are five of Sir Roger's strongly marked beliefs?
6. How do our conceptions of a gentleman differ from those of Sir Roger's day?
7. Select what you consider the outstanding trait of Sir Roger, discuss it, and illustrate it.
8. With the exception of Sir Roger, who do you think was the most admirable character in these papers? Defend your choice.
9. Write a brief character sketch of Will Honeycomb. Does his character develop, or does it remain static?
10. Give five characters introduced in these papers whose names are suggestive of the men themselves.
11. The *Spectator* papers have been called the forerunners of the novel. Explain.

12. Name four characteristics of a good essay, and show how well one of the *DeCoverley Papers* meets these requirements.

13. You have just made a trip to the England of Queen Anne's day. Write a letter to a friend, describing your outstanding experiences on this trip.

14. Summarize what you have learned about one feature of the life of these times; for example, the dress, the theaters, the modes of travel, rural life, the coffee-houses.

15. Give four reasons why you should (or should not) like to live at the time of Addison and Steele.

16. Summarize briefly the history of the Queen Anne period, stressing the political issues of the time.

17. Explain the differences between a Whig and a Tory.

18. What was there in the history and politics of the time putting Sir Roger and Sir Andrew in opposition?

19. In what three ways can you contrast the characters of Addison and Steele?

20. What distinction does the Spectator make between manners and morals?

21. What were Addison and Steele's methods of reform? How did these men differ from many other reformers?

22. State four lessons or principles of character improvement suggested by these essays.

23. State three facts about the style of Addison and Steele as shown in these Papers.

24. Who or what were the following: *assizes*, *quorum*, *Prince Eugene*, *white witch*, *Roundheads and Cavaliers*, *yeomen*, *tithe-stealers*, *knight of the shire*, *Eton*, *Inner Temple*, *Soho Square?*

FOR THE ENGLISH LABORATORY.

A class in science which went no further in its particular subject than to study one text and to recite upon its contents would be thought a very poorly trained set of pupils indeed in these days when microscopes, test tubes, and air pumps are the common equipment of the science department. Similarly, a well-selected library is necessary for the mastery of certain books. Not all books indeed: Long John Silver stamping and stumping the deck of the *Hispaniola* appeals to any reader who chances to pick up a copy of *Treasure Island;* the story needs little or no comment. But with the *Spectator* papers it is different; we must equip ourselves to read these with understanding, for not till we have done this will they yield us their fascination and delight. We must relive these interesting days when Steele and Addison loitered in the coffee-houses, when sedan chairs bore bewigged beaux and patched and powdered belles to the theater, or to the gaming tables, or to the court, where Whigs and Tories waged their wars of politics as vigorously as their great duke, Marlborough, waged his brilliant campaigns against the proud French Louis. With historian and antiquary and with novelist and poet as guides we must thread the narrow, smoky London streets, watch the people at their work and their play, and bump over miserable roads out to the homes of the English squires. If we are willing to pay the price in time and labor, we shall reap a rich harvest. The following are some of the most valuable books for our English laboratory equipment.

G. Gregory Smith's edition of the *Spectator*, which fills four volumes of the Everyman's Library (Dutton) is one of the cheapest and most desirable sets of this essential material. Less necessary, but desirable, is the four-volume edition of the *Tatler* edited by George A. Aitken. Wendell and Greenough's *Selections from Addison* and G. R. Carpenter's *Selections from Steele* (Ginn), both in the Athenæum Press series, contain excellent introductions and many valuable notes. *Selections from the Tatler, the Spectator, and Their Successors* by Walter Graham (Nelson) is a very convenient and valuable volume. A beautiful and attractive illustrated edition is *Sir Roger de Coverley and Other Essays from the Spectator*, illustrated by Brock and published by Dent. Equally attractive are *Days with Sir Roger*, illustrated by Hugh Thomson for the Macmillan Company, and *The Spectator in London*, fifty-six illustrations by Ralph Cleoner (Lippincott). Illustrative materials may also be secured from the Thompson Publishing Company, Syracuse, New York, and from Raphael Tuck and Sons, 122 Fifth Avenue, New York City. *The Advertisements of the Spectator* (Houghton), by L. Lewis, will furnish much interesting information.

The best biography of Addison is W. J. Courthope's in the *English Men of Letters* (Macmillan); the most famous, perhaps, is Macaulay's *Essay on Addison* (Heath). Austin Dobson's *Richard Steele* in the English Worthies (Appleton) is a delightful volume, as is also *The Letters of Richard Steele* (Dodd), edited by R. Brimley Johnson.

Among the most valuable histories of the time are the following: Gardiner, S. R., *A Student's History of England* (Longmans Green); Green, J. R., *Short History of the English People* (Everyman, Dutton); Burton, J. H., *History of the Reign of Queen Anne*, Chaps. II, XVIII, XIX; Lecky, W. E. H., *A History of England in the Eighteenth Century*, Chaps. I, II, IV. The third chapter of Macaulay's *History of England* should be read by every member of the class.

To peruse Swift's *Journal to Stella*, Bohn's Standard Library (Harcourt, Brace) comes our nearest, perhaps, to actually seeing the life and age. Herbert Paul's *Queen Anne* (Hodder and Stoughton) is a valuable book. Three great mines of information are John Ashton's *Social England in the Reign of Queen Anne* (Scribner), W. C. Sydney's *England and the English in the Eighteenth Century*, and A. S. Turberville's *English Men and Manners in the Eighteenth Century* (Oxford). Sir Walter Besant's illustrated record, *London in the Eighteenth Century* (Black) is an expensive but a valuable book; the same may be said of E. B. Chancellor's *The XVIII Century in London* (Scribner).

Thackeray's *Henry Esmond*, which has been called "the best historical novel ever written," portrays the times admirably, as does also his *English Humorists of the Eighteenth Century* (Heath). Austin Dobson's verses — *At the Sign of the Lyre* or his *Complete Poetical Works* (Oxford) give many attractive sketches of life in the days of Anne. Here two well illustrated books demand and deserve honorable mention: *Trivia, or the Art of Walking the Streets of London*, by John Gay, with an introduction and notes by W. H. Williams (D. O'Connor, London, 1922), and *John Gay's London, Illustrated from the Poetry of the Times* by William Henry Irving (Harvard University Press), 1927.

Austin Dobson's *Eighteenth Century Essays* and his *Eighteenth Century Vignettes*, Third Series (Oxford) are to be recommended as are also Edmund Gosse's *History of English Literature of the Eighteenth Century* (Macmillan) and Oliver Elton's *Augustan Ages* (Scribner).

A. J. C. Hare's *Walks in London* (McKay) is a mine of information concerning that great city; and Helen M. Pratt's *Westminster Abbey*, 2 vols. (Duffield) is a thoroughly delightful and reliable treatment of its subject.

FOR PROJECTS AND FOR INDIVIDUALIZED INSTRUCTION.

The following subjects offer interesting and valuable work in projects for the entire class or for pupils in classes where the highest grades are given to such as complete successfully such additional tasks.

1. Further readings in the *Spectator*. Among the many topics appearing in the *DeCoverley Papers* deserving further investigation and report, the following may be suggested, together with the most important papers in connection with each:

(*a*) The Spectator does not hesitate at times to talk frankly with the reader concerning matters relating to his publication. Many references will be found scattered through the papers, but the following numbers will be especially fruitful: 10, 101, 232, 445, 448, 544, 555, 556, 632.

(*b*) Nos. 324 and 347 deal with the Mohawks; No. 28 is an interesting account of street signs. Nos. 9, 26, 50, 69, 72, 477, and 631 all present matters of value concerning London and London life.

(*c*) The customs of the ladies of the time are pictured in Nos. 37, 81, 102, 265, 295, 281, 323, 435, and elsewhere.

(*d*) The best of the visions and allegories, another popular type in the *Spectator*, appear in Nos. 3, 159, 584, 585.

(*e*) Various phases of the Spectator's attitude toward literature may be found in Nos. 70, 124, 135, 158, 235; and on matters of religion, including the famous paraphrases of the *Psalms*, in 111, 441, 465, 494.

2. Interesting materials found in the *Tatler*.
3. Resemblances and differences in content and in style between the *Tatler* and the *Spectator*.
4. A summary, either oral or written, of materials dealing with the politics of the age as found in some history of the times.
5. Eighteenth-century life as pictured in *Henry Esmond*.
6. Richard Steele as shown in his letters.
7. A reading of Austin Dobson's poems of eighteenth-century life.
8. More information concerning Westminster Abbey.
9. Reports, either oral or written, on eighteenth-century amusements, meals, crimes, funerals, dress, modes of travel, coffee-houses, etc.
10. The literary notables in the Age of Anne.
11. The Age of Anne as pictured in the *Journal to Stella*.
12. Who is who in the *Spectator Papers?*
13. A dictionary of unfamiliar terms appearing in these papers.
14. A series of papers in the style of the *Spectator*, dealing with current events or with present-day topics.
15. A series of papers in which the Spectator records his impressions of various features of your community.
16. A collection of pictures illustrating the life and the times.
17. A set of original drawings illustrating the *Spectator*.
18. A set of six posters for the bulletin board.
19. A musical program, with instrumental and vocal music popular in those times. Dancing the minuet.
20. An eighteenth-century program for a school assembly.

21. A dramatization of an evening either at the Club or at the home of Sir Roger.

22. A debate: Resolved that the Age of Anne would have been a more desirable time in which to live than the Age of Elizabeth.

23. A model of a typical coffee-house.

24. An eighteenth-century style show.

25. An eighteenth-century party.

26. A large map of London for the bulletin board, showing the location of various coffee-houses, theaters, churches, palaces, etc.

27. A study of the advertisements in the *Spectator*.